THE HURRICANE'S CHILDREN

by Carl Carmer

STARS FELL ON ALABAMA

LISTEN FOR A LONESOME DRUM

DARK TREES TO THE WIND

AMERICA SINGS

MY KIND OF COUNTRY

THE TAVERN LAMPS ARE BURNING, *Compiler*

The

Hurricane's Children

by

CARL CARMER

Illustrated by Elizabeth Black Carmer

DAVID McKAY COMPANY, Inc.

New York

Library of Congress Catalog Card Number: 67-17525

MANUFACTURED IN THE UNITED STATES OF AMERICA

Blood's my natural drink—and the wails of the dying is music to my ears. I'm the original iron-jawed, brass-mounted corpse-maker—sired by a hurricane, dammed by an earthquake, half brother to the smallpox.

I'm a ringtail dazzler and a swivel-backed lallapaloosa! I'm half wild horse and half crocodile! I'm a roarin' ripsnorter and chock-full o' fight! I can wrastle a buffalo and chaw the ear off a grizzly!!!

I'm a child o' the snappin' turtle, raised on alligator meat and weaned on panther's milk! I can outrun, outjump, outshoot, outdrink, throw down, hog-tie, rough-and-tumble and no holds barred, drag out and lick any man on both sides of the river from Pittsburgh to New Orleans! Y-i-i-i-i-p-peeeee!!!

I'm a ring-tailed squealer and my name is Fight!! I'm an old brown bear that can claw the stuffin' out'n a buckeye! And I scratch my head with lightnin'!!!

War and bloodshed puts muscle on my bones! An' every lick I take with an ax lets in an acre o' sunshine! Come on, you flatboaters, you bargers, and see how tough I can chew. I ain't had a fight fer two hours! I'll bite yer feet off and sling your heads in the Gulf o' Mexico! Y-i-i-i-eee!!!

To

ZOE AND HENRY CHRISTMAN

CONTENTS

THE BLUE SNOWMAN

FOURTH OF JULY IN NORTH DAKOTA

PREFACE

IN trying to describe this book when I first talked about doing it I said it was a group of American fairy stories. I have waited to see what it would turn out to be before writing the preface, and now that it is done I find that there are no fairies in it. Instead, I find a lot of giants proudly roaring that a hurricane was their father and an earthquake was their mother.

The people of almost every nation in the world except the United States have liked to make up stories about "the little people." Even the American Indians tell some beautiful tales about them. But Americans have been so busy doing big jobs that they have never taken time off to let their minds play with the tiny folk who have magic powers. At the end of a hard day's work the American cowboys or miners or lumberjacks or applepickers have had their fun out of making up stories about men who could do jobs that just could not be done, and in an impossibly short time with one hand tied behind them. The dreams of American workers, naturally enough, have never been delicate, exquisite, or polite—like many fairy stories. They have been big and powerful, and a strong wind is always blowing through them. And so I have discovered that this is not an American fairy-story book at all, but an American giant book.

If these stories had existed hundreds of years ago in another land we would probably be calling them myths today and reading of Pecos Bill and Tony Beaver and Annie Christmas as we read of Mercury and Mars and Juno, or of Thor and Loki and Freya. The stories in this book are the products of our grandfathers' fancies, our fathers', our own. They are the imagination that Americans inherit, and I hope many young Americans are going to be proud of it.

The speeches with which I have chosen to begin the various sections of the book are, like the tales, samples of American imagination when it is used on a certain locality. Although they were not written as verses, these speeches are a kind of highfaluting poetry made up by men who love to sing out in praise of the place they live in, and who love also the sound of their own deep-sounding American voices. So many people have asked me for the words to "Change the Name of

Arkansas?" or the "Lecture on the Petrified Forest" that I thought I had better include in each section the speech that folks remember and like to hear.

I have tried to tell the tales simply and in the kind of language in which American folks still tell them. I have not tried to do more than give a little hint once in a while of the way single words sound in the part of the country the story comes from, but I have tried to imitate the swing of them when they are put together and talked off by the fireside.

I owe a great debt to the patient workers in American folklore who have collected these stories. Although they are here told, wherever it is possible, as they have been told to me by folks throughout the country, in a number of cases I would not even have known of the giant who lives in the hearts and minds of the people of a locality if somebody who lives and writes there had not told me about him. And so my heartiest thanks to the writers of all the books and pamphlets listed in the bibliography at the end of this book.

I want to express my particular gratitude to Paul R. Beath for permission to use the materials he has gathered on Febold Feboldson, to Charles

Edward Brown for his friendly help on the Tony Beaver legends, to J. Frank Dobie for his generous aid and for his permission to use the results of his research on the legend of the White Mustang, to Frank Shay for his permission to use the material included in his admirable book, *Here's Audacity! American Legendary Heroes*, to Jeremiah Digges, author of *The Cape Cod Pilot*, for his help on the legend of Ichabod Paddock, to L. M. A. Roy for telling me the story of Ocean-Born Mary.

C. C.

THE MIDDLE OF THE WORLD

Mr. Speaker—you blue-bellied, cross-eyed jackass. I have for the last thirty minutes been trying to get your attention and each time I have caught your eyes, you have wormed, twisted, and squirmed like a dog with a flea in his hide.

Hear me, gentlemen, the world will pause and wonder at the death-defying audacity of this lop-eared, lantern-jawed, half-breed, whisky-soaked hyena who has proposed to change the name of Arkansas.

Compare the lily of the valley to the gorgeous sunrise, the discordant croak of the bullfrog to the melodious tones of a nightingale; the classic strains of Mozart to the bray of a Mexican mule; the puny arm of a Peruvian prince to the muscles of a Roman gladiator—but change the name of Arkansas? Never!

Hide the stars in a nail keg, turn the moon out to pasture, extract your sunshine from cucumbers, put the sky to soak in a gourd, hang the Arkansas River on a clothesline; unbuckle the bellyband of time—but change the name of Arkansas? Hell-fire, No!

HOW MIKE FINK LOST HIS GIRL

The Ohio River country is peaceful and sunny, with sycamores lining the gentle winding streams and hollyhocks lining the paths that lead to farm doors crowned with morning-glory vines. The people who live in Tobasco, Vinegar Switch, Blue Fly, and Getaway recall the tales of the rough-and-ready bully boys of the keelboat days with hearty affection.

MIKE FINK was one of the Ohio River boatmen in the early days of transport—before the paddle-wheel steamers—when freight was moved down the Ohio on keelboats by manpower. Poling the boat back upstream after a cargo had been delivered was tough work that required tough men. Well, Mike was the toughest of the lot. Folks tell he was never satisfied to lick his weight in wildcats. He'd feel that he was takin' an unfair advantage if he wasn't lickin' at least *ten times* his weight in wildcats. He used to shoot the topknots off wild Indians just for fun, and they say he could shoot the combs out of a girl's hair at twenty rods without disarranging a single strand. When he was on the river, he used to amuse himself by shooting off the little curlicue tails of baby pigs on the bank with one shot.

Mike was a great jumper and only made one mistake in judging the distance he could leap. That was when he tried to jump the Ohio where it runs into the Mississippi near Cairo, Illinois. He got about halfway across and realized he wasn't going to reach the other side, so he just turned around in the air, quick as you please, and got back to the shore he started from

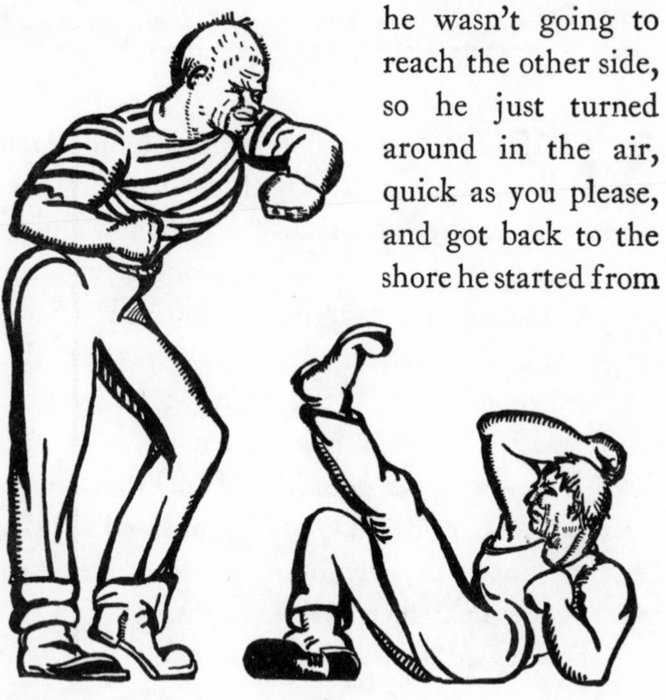

dry, except for a wet left foot that landed a little behind his right.

Mike got arrested once for a minor crime and his friends begged him to stand trial just for the dignity of the community. He said he would feel embarrassed standing trial without a boat under him. The sheriff said he understood about that and he provided a wagon on which Mike and his men loaded their keelboat. Then they all poled the boat up the steep bank to the courthouse. There, on his own boat deck, Mike stood trial and was acquitted. Just as his men raised a cheer, however, the judge said:

"I have here another indictment charging you with shooting a flatboatman."

"I ain't standin' trial for breakin' no game laws," said Mike. "Reverse poles," he ordered his men, and the wagon began to coast down the bank. Before the sheriff knew what had happened his wagon had rolled into the river and Mike and his boatmen were floating down the Ohio.

The story of how Mike Fink lost his girl is the only one I know about Mike in which he got the worst of it, but they say he used to tell it himself, so I guess it must be true.

One hot day Mike decided to go swimming in Butcherknife Creek. He left Peg, his sunburned, homespun-clad bride-to-be, at the deacon's house for the usual Wednesday afternoon prayer meeting and then walked across the deacon's meadow to the swimming hole. He had just stripped to his red flannel underwear (which he wore the year round) when the deacon's bull happened to notice his aggravatin' figure.

Mike had just time to jump out of the way when the bull went by him so fast that the wind he created blew all the clothes Mike had just taken off into the creek. That convinced Mike that the safest place for him to be was behind that bull—so when the infuriated animal charged again, Mike leaped high in the air and grasped the bull's upright tail as it went by. The bull bellowed and raced around the lot, but Mike held on and would have been safe enough for some time if the deacon's two vicious watchdogs hadn't heard the noise and come to investigate. They didn't recognize Mike in his red underwear and attached to the bull's tail, so they followed along behind, barking and occasionally catching up enough to bite Mike.

I don't know how long this would have con-

tinued if another accident hadn't occurred. The bull was so mad he kept switching his tail around and up and down. Well, just as they passed under the branches of the old apple tree in the southeast corner of the deacon's lot, the bull raised his tail high in the air. Mike hung on and went with it. There was a hornets' nest hanging from one of the lower limbs and Mike just naturally went through it headfirst. The bull made a quick turn and started for the deacon's house, and now the noises in the fast-moving parade were louder and there were more of them.

The prayer meeting folks just couldn't imagine what was happening out there in the meadow. First there would be the bull's bellow, then the dogs barking and snapping, then Mike hollering, and then the loud buzzing of a swarm of mad hornets.

The bull had reached the deacon's yard now, and just as the folks in the prayer meeting were fetching up against the fence outside to see what the fuss was for, Mike took a header off the bull's tail and landed in the middle of these good people in his red flannel underwear. And the hornets were right on top of everybody in no time. They got busy. By the time the deacon and Peg and the rest of them had got the hornets out of their hair they began to swell up like dry sponges in a tub o' water. Peg's eyes swelled shut and she said that even if they went down to natural again she could never see her way clear to marryin' Mike Fink. She said she figured Mike had plumb humiliated her.

So Mike went back to the Ohio River and never had anything more to do with women after the day he lost his girl through no fault of his own. He and his men got on their keelboat and started out from the mouth of Butcherknife Creek singing this song:

> Hard upon the beach oar!
> She moves too slow—
> All the way to Shawneetown,
> Long time ago.

HOW DAVY CROCKETT FIDDLED HIS DAUGHTER OUT OF A HUSBAND

You can hear some mighty clever stories about Davy Crockett in Tennessee where he was born and in Kentucky and Texas where he fought and hunted, but the place where he seemed to be himself more than any other was in Arkansas. Just ask the folks that live in Lone Sassafras, Smackover, Cowmound, and Nellie's Apron.

DAVY CROCKETT was the greatest bear hunter of his day, or any other, and he never felt above a personal wrestling match with an old he-bear. Most Americans know about the Davy Crockett of history—the frontiersman, congressman, soldier, who was born in Tennessee and died so gallantly in the desperate and hopeless Texas battle of the Alamo. But not enough of us know that in Arkansas Davy found a country just to his liking and sort of branched out in ways that made his career even more astonishing.

He was such a great hunter that for ordinary

game like a big coon or even a medium-sized bear he never bothered to use his gun—he just grinned them down out of the trees and let the dogs settle them. Arkansas folks say he once mistook a big knot on a branch for a coon and grinned hard at it —so hard that, although no coon fell out of the tree, all the bark came off the knot.

Davy was also, like Mike Fink in Ohio, a great jumper. Whenever he got far away from home he used to jump on the sun and catch a ride back to his Arkansas cabin. One day he miscalculated himself east of his cabin when he was really west and had to stay on for twenty-two hours to get back around home.

I suppose no American ever trained a more unlikely lot of wild animal pets than Davy Crockett. His favorite was his big black bear, Death Hug, but he liked his shaggy buffalo, Mississip, too. Mississip was a sensitive animal gifted with a deep rumbling bass voice that he used to good advantage whenever Davy and a few of the boys got together to sing *Hail Columbia* or possibly *The Bride's Farewell.* Nobody could hit the deep notes half so well as old Mississip.

As for Death Hug, he was a powerful animal and a great skater. Folks around Fort Smith still tell about the cold winter day when Death Hug and Davy and a Kentucky friend of theirs named Ben Hardin put on skates and went out on the frozen Arkansas River to play snap the whip. Death Hug went so fast that the ice got hot and a spark struck from it by one of his skates hit Davy Crockett's rifle and made it go off. That surprised the three of them so that their feet went out from under them and they all sat down on the ice. They had been going so fast that they slid all the way to Pine Bluff in a seated posture before they could stop. Crowds lined the banks at Little Rock to see them go by.

The first time that Davy Crockett and Ben Hardin met there was the dickens to pay. They took one look at each other and trouble began. Somebody made up a song about the fight that took place—and I think it was Ben Hardin. It goes like this:

As I walked out by the light of the moon,
I met Colonel Davy goin' out a-coonin';
I asked him for his gun and he said he hadn't none—
Says I, "Colonel Davy you ought to have one."
Ha! Ha! Ha!

You go along with Colonel Davy,
And he'll show you how to grin a coon crazy!

Oh, I pinned back my ears an' I puffed like a steamer,
Says I, "Colonel Davy, I'm a Kaintuck Screamer."

Then we both locked horns an' I thought my breath
was gone,
For I never fit so hard since the day I was born.
Ha! Ha! Ha!

We fit half a day and then agreed to stop it,
For I was licked bad—and so was Davy Crockett!

Ben Hardin and Davy Crockett became fast friends after that fight and had many wild adventures together. The only thing about Ben that worried Davy was his eye for the beautiful Arkansas ladies, and particularly for Davy's own daughter—who was as handsome and spirited a nineteen-year-old as there was in the whole state.

Ben Hardin said: "She's prettier than a dolphin, and I've seen a dolphin."

"You can have her," says Davy, "if you can dance her down."

"I can dance harder and fancier and longer than any *ten* gals," said Ben, and he and Davy began getting things ready.

Davy got his fiddle and told his pet bear, Death Hug, and his pet buffalo, Mississip, to come along to make another couple in the set.

They all went down to the Asphaltum Flats that are so smooth and hard that lightning just slides off when it strikes them.

"I'll start in playin' *Arkansas Traveller*," said Davy, "and then I'll play *Whole Hog or None* and *Indian Squaw* and *That Big Black Bar'll Git You, Honey*, and so on till I've played the nine hundred ninety-nine fiddle tunes I know —and then I'll start over again. I'll do the callin' while I'm fiddlin' on this here hemlock fiddle."

Then Davy began to fiddle and to call out the dance steps, like this:

All t' your places and straighten up your faces,
Let out your belt bands an' tighten up your traces,
Balance All!

Squirrel hop out and owl hoot in,
Three arms round an' a hootin' again.

By this time Ben Hardin was pretty excited. He was doing a neat buck-and-wing on the corners, and old Death Hug, the bear, was swinging his partner round in the air, and Mississip, the buffalo, was bowing mighty pretty.

Davy kept on calling:

Runnin' up the river Injun style,
Gals in the lead and gents plumb wild!

And every once in a while Ben would interrupt with an exclamation like: "Daddy ketch a rat!" or "Shake them rattles off!"

> Allemand left an' back t' your taw,
> An' acrost t' the gal from Arkansaw!

sang Davy.

"That's me," screamed Davy's daughter, and Ben shouted: "Allemandy goodelum— All chaw hay!"

> Log chain your sweetie an' stay chain your honey,
> Double up, boys, git the worth o' your money!

sang Davy, and Ben answered: "Grabble my taters!"

> Gents' hands in your pockets and backs to the wall,
> Take a chaw o' tobacco an' balance all!

sang Davy.

That dance, ladies and gentlemen, lasted three days an' nights, and Davy was on his nine hundred and thirty-first tune on the second time round before Ben Hardin started waverin' some. He was still making a brave effort to do a few show-off steps on the corners, though. And Davy's girl was stepping the figures off as pretty an' as

fresh as a cornflower in a spring breeze. Then all of a sudden Ben Hardin went down. He started to bow low and he fell flat on his face. He tried to get up but he couldn't make it. Davy stopped fiddlin'.

"Well, Ben Hardin," he said, "if you can't dance her down you can't marry my gal."

"Ben's no good, pa," said Davy's gal. "Let's go somewhere and dance."

"You can keep your gal, Crockett," said Ben. "I'd as soon marry a young tornado."

Unfortunately a young female tornado happened to be raisin' a ruckus around Arkansas at that very moment, overheard Ben Hardin's derogatory remark, and set out boilin' right after him. The first thing Davy Crockett or any of the dancers knew, lightning was ricocheting off the Asphaltum Flats all around them and they could see that insulted tornado bearin' down on 'em at a terrific rate.

"We got just one chance," Davy Crockett said, speaking very calmly as he always did when he was in danger. "The next lightnin' that cracks down on us we'll have to get a good holt on and ride it away from here."

Just then a big bolt hit right close to them,

and Davy and his daughter, Ben Hardin and Death Hug and Mississip had just time to jump aboard before it ricocheted off towards Texarkana and took them with it—out of the way of that tornado. It was a mighty rough ride for a while until Davy got out his little bottle of rattlesnake oil that he always carried and smoothed out the lightning some with it. You've heard people talk about something happening "as quick as greased lightning," haven't you? Well, that's where they got the expression—from Davy Crockett's oiling that bolt of lightning with rattlesnake grease.

HOW THE EDUCATED BULLDOG SAID TOO MUCH

The bulldog of this story has appeared in a good many forms in the history of world's folk stories. Indianians tell the story with real pride, and somehow it seems to fit into the way Indiana folks (folks who live in Farmer's Retreat, Steam Corner, Home Place, Cumback) look at things.

INDIANA corn is said by those who know (and *who* should know as well as Indianians?) to grow faster and have a better flavor than any other kind. I don't quite know whether or not to believe a farmer of French descent who lived near Vincennes who said that he almost laughed himself to death when he was sowing corn because the sprouts came up from the seeds so fast that they tickled his feet. He said he went to the house to call his hired man, and when he came out the corn had already eared at a height of about thirty feet. He sent the hired man climbing up a stalk after the ears, and by the time he'd got up thirty feet the corn was growing so fast the ear was thirty feet higher. The hired man climbed on up and finally got so high he was out of sight. The farmer said he hollered to him to start back, and he said he'd been trying to, but the corn was growing faster than he could come down and he was getting higher all the time. He never did get down, and the farmer never saw him again. This particular stalk, the farmer said, happened to be popcorn, and when the ears got up so close to the sun the heat was so great that all the kernels popped and fell all over his hayfield. He said a mule that was standing hitched to a hayrake in that field mistook all those white popcorn kernels for a June snowstorm and just naturally lay down and froze to death.

This same farmer had a son of whose ability he was very proud, and the son had a bulldog. When the boy was eighteen years old the farmer sent him way across the state to Earlham College to get an education. The boy took the bulldog along for company. After the boy and the dog had been at Earlham a month or so, the old man received a letter from his son.

This is what the boy wrote:

"Father, an astonishing thing has happened.

The bulldog has begun to talk. Moreover, he seems to have a fairly good mind. I'd like to make a suggestion to you. If we educated the bulldog along with me here at Earlham, we'd have at the end of four years not only the one talking bulldog in the world, but the one and only talking bulldog with a college education. We could exhibit him then all over Indiana, charge admission, and make a lot of money. If you agree with me, father, just send me double the usual amount of money for books, laboratory fees, incidentals, and miscellaneous. It will be a mighty good investment."

So for four years the farmer sent his son double the usual amount for the usual items, and finally the day came when his son and the remarkable bulldog were to return home with their college degrees. The boy wrote that the bulldog had made an outstanding record at Earlham and had taken honors in two subjects. He said that he and the dog would travel by train to Vincennes and then hire a boat to take them downriver to the farm.

The old man got very excited on the day they were due to arrive and he waited anxiously on the bank as the little boat approached. When the boy jumped ashore his father clasped him in his arms

—and then he looked about him and said: "And where's our educated bulldog?"

"Well, father," said the boy, "it was as I said. The bulldog graduated with honors and then we both took the train for Vincennes. When we got there, I hired a boat to bring us here. And on the way down, I said to the bulldog, 'Isn't it wonderful, in less than an hour, now, we'll be back with my father?'

" 'What, that stupid, uneducated old ignoramus?' said the bulldog, and, father, it made me so angry to hear him speak so insultingly of you that I kicked him overboard. He couldn't swim a stroke and so he was drowned."

Well, that's the story—sworn to as gospel truth by a lot of respectable Indianians—so I guess it must be so. They say that the father was convinced it was true, praised his son for being so loyal to his old dad, and gave him a home-coming play party that night at the farmhouse that folks remember to this day.

THAR SHE BLOWS

Mr. Speaker—allow me to picture to your denuded imagination some of the heartrending evils which arise from want of proper protection to hen roosts amongst my constituents. Mr. Speaker, we will suppose it to be the awful and melancholy hour of midnight—the solemn wind softly moans through waving branches of the trees and naught is heard to break the stillness—save an occasional grunt from the hogpen. I will now carry you in imagination to the peaceful henhouse. Behold its happy inmates in balmy slumber on their elevated roosts. Is there anything so mean and sneaking as robbery of such a home? I answer in thunder tones, Mr. Speaker—NO! There is not!

You may search the wide universe, from the natives who repose in solitary grandeur and superlative majesty under the shade of the tall cedars that grow upon the tops of the Himalaya Mountains or in the valley of Jehoshaphat down to the degraded and barbarous savages who repose in obscurity in their miserable hovels on the Rock of Gibraltar or in the Gulf of Mexico, and you will not find anything so mean. All I want, Mr. Speaker, is for every member of this legislature to act on this subject according to his conscience. Let him do this and he will be remembered everlastingly by a grateful posterity.

Mr. Speaker, I have done! Where's my hat?

(Adapted from the Speech of Lot Doolittle on the Bill for the Protection of Hen Roosts as found in *Dr. Valentine and Yankee Hill's Metamorphoses* published in 1850.)

HOW OCEAN-BORN MARY CAME BACK FROM THE DEAD

Ocean-Born Mary is known mostly to New Hampshire. Folks outside the state are just beginning to hear of her. But the citizens of Swanzey and Noon and Pine Valley and Snowville can tell about her and add a bit of their own to a story of pirates and ghosts.

NO state has more tales of witches and ghosts with which to while away the winter evenings than New Hampshire. And of all the tales of New Hampshire ghosts, I like best the story of Ocean-Born Mary. I like it so much that I made a visit to the haunted house in which folks say her ghost still walks, and I heard her story from the lips of eighty-year-old Mrs. Roy who lives there.

I arrived at the house, which is on the side of a steep mountain south of the village of Henniker, just at twilight. Mrs. Roy was in the yard gathering herbs, but she kindly led me through the old green doorway built many years before the American Revolution. We sat in the front room, the eagle room, she calls it, because someone, possibly Ocean-Born Mary herself, painted above the fireplace long ago an American eagle with a band of sixteen stars above him. There she told me the story while the light left the New Hampshire hills and the room grew gray and dark and the white-spindled old stairway to the second story creaked mysteriously.

In the year 1720 Mrs. Roy said, a group of emigrants from Londonderry, Ireland, took ship for America, expecting to join relatives and friends living in Londonderry, New Hampshire. As they were nearing the Massachusetts coast a sinister-looking frigate flying no flag bore down upon their unarmed boat, fired a gun across her bows, forcing her to heave to. Then, while the crew stood helpless, white and silent, and the emigrants kneeled on the deck in prayer for deliverance, a boat put out from the stranger bearing sunburned men. They clambered aboard the emigrant ship, terrified the passengers and crew with their weapons, and bound them securely.

Their leader, whom they called Captain Pedro, was a tall dark man who said little. Though he looked Spanish he talked perfect English when he ordered his captives to prepare for immediate death. As he spoke, a faint cry came from below deck, and he suddenly wheeled about and hastened down the companionway. In a cabin below he came upon a mother and her newborn girl baby. He said to her: "Madam, if I may be allowed to name this little girl after my own mother, I will not harm this ship or its passengers." The mother gladly gave consent, and the pirate captain said: "Her name shall be Mary."

Then he went back on deck and ordered all the captives released and his own men into their boat. In a few moments he was on his way back to the frigate. Just as the emigrants were rejoicing over their good fortune, however, they were again panic-stricken by the captain's return. He carried with him a bolt of grayish green tapestry silk, exquisitely embroidered in a flower pattern. He strode down to the mother's cabin. "For your little daughter's wedding dress," he said, and returned to his boat.

The emigrants landed safely, but soon thereafter in Boston Ocean-Born Mary's father died. Then the mother took the little girl into the New Hampshire hills. More than a score of years went by, and Ocean-Born Mary was a wife and herself the mother of four boys. She was six feet tall now, with red hair, very white skin, and green eyes. All over the state people talked of her beauty. And many grieved for her when she was left a widow with her four small sons to bring up.

But Captain Pedro had never forgotten the girl named for his mother. He was getting old now and longed for a more peaceful life—somewhere distant from the scenes of his criminal career. And so he came to Henniker to build a peaceful refuge from his own past and to be near his mother's namesake. He brought with him black slaves and his ship's carpenters and a few of his pirate crew. They chose a spot completely out of sight of any human dwelling and there they built a stately Colonial house with high handrailings on the stair like those on the bridge of the captain's ship and a sloping floor in the rear rooms like the slanting surface of a deck. Then he invited Ocean-Born Mary to come to live in the house, take care of him in his old age, and bring up her sons there. She accepted and became a fitting and beautiful mistress of the stately house. The captain presented her with a coach-and-four, and neighbors smiled to see her riding in it with her four tall sons. One day the captain returned from the seacoast with an enormous wooden chest.

At midnight he and one of his pirate men staggered out of the high side door of the house carrying it on their shoulders, and Ocean-Born Mary heard the sound of shovels in the earth, then a low groan, and silence. The captain came back to the house alone and no one ever saw his pirate helper again.

It was over a year later that Ocean-Born Mary came home from a drive in her coach one late afternoon to find the house deserted. But in the orchard behind the house she found the body of the captain. He had been run through with a sailor's cutlass. She had her slaves bring the body into the house and there she supervised the captain's burial under the eight-by-three-foot stone slab in front of the big kitchen hearth—just as he had directed her to do in case of his death.

Ocean-Born Mary lived on in the old house. Her sons, grown to be men and all of them over six-foot-eight, left her to fight against the British king in the American Revolution. When they returned they took houses of their own. But Ocean-Born Mary lived on alone in the big house until 1814, when she died at the age of ninety-four.

The house was long unoccupied after that.

Then people began to talk about the strange things that went on there. They still do. They say that strange lights appear in the windows at midnight. Some curious folks who went there at twilight claimed that they saw a very tall woman of great beauty walking down the high-railinged stair. Others say that on warm spring nights just after darkness has followed the twilight, a coach-and-four drives up to the old entrance and a tall woman steps out and hurries into the house. Immediately after that there come, from the old orchard back of the house, fearful groans as of a man in mortal pain.

Mediums and other people who claim supernatural power frequently visit Mrs. Roy in the old house. Some of them say that surely there is something of mysterious interest under the eight-by-three stone slab in the kitchen. I asked Mrs. Roy why she didn't have the slab lifted to see if the bones of the captain are there. She said that it would cost a hundred and fifty dollars and she thought that so much money as that would buy a lot of things more useful to her than a skeleton. One of the mediums not long ago said that she had summoned up the captain's spirit and talked to it. She said that she told the captain Mrs. Roy

was a nice lady and that he ought to let her know somehow where his treasure is buried—but the captain just said: "I buried it. Let her *find* it."

When I heard all this for the first time I thought somebody had just made up a fancy story for me that had few words of truth in it. But now that I have seen a piece of Ocean-Born Mary's wedding gown—the gray-green silk embroidered in a flower pattern—and the strange eight-by-three hearthstone that looks like the top of a coffin with a hole drilled in the middle of it—and the house itself looking dark and haunted in the late twilight—and listened to Mrs. Roy—I'm not sure where truth ends and fancy begins. At any rate, many folks in New Hampshire love to tell this story on winter evenings before their birch-log fires, or on their porches on summer evenings when the stars are very bright above the mountaintops.

HOW OLD STORMALONG WHITENED THE CLIFFS OF DOVER

Old Stormalong has been known all over Massachusetts for a long time from the song sailors sing about him. And every time somebody thinks up a good salty yarn it's pretty sure to end up fastened on Stormie's broad back. It can hold up a fair load. Try listening to what they say about him in Horseneck Beach, Swapstone, Sixteen Acres, or Mystic Junction.

ONE name that all good salts recognize with affection and respect is that of the superable seaman, bosun extra-peculiar, captain ne plus ultra, Old Stormalong—the biggest man that ever shipped before a mast, the most powerful deepwater sailorman who ever holystoned a deck. I've heard tell he was born in New Bedford, but some folks claim he came from Barnstable or Wellfleet or some other one of those Cape Cod towns.

The first time Alfred Bulltop Stormalong attracted considerable attention to himself was when the boat he was on was out for whales and had anchored somewhere in the North Atlantic. Stormie was bosun then. The lookout saw what looked like a school of whales off on the horizon and Stormie ordered all hands for'ard to hist the mudhook. His men heaved and heaved, but they couldn't get that anchor off the bottom. It would give a bit, and then something would pull it back down. Once they got it so far up, though, that they could see what was causing the difficulty. A giant octopus had satcheled onto the hook and was holdin' on for dear life with a dozen legs while his other dozen kept tight hold on the bottom.

Well, before you could say Jack Robinson, Old Stormalong dived overboard right on top of that octopus. Then there was a rollin' and a boilin' such as nobody ever saw in mid-ocean before. The boat stood on her beam ends and pitched and tossed like she was in the middle of the great-grandaddy of all the Atlantic squalls. Then, all of a sudden, everything was calm again and up came Old Stormie from the bottom of the sea. He grabbed the anchor chain and came swinging aboard hand over hand.

"Lift her now," he said, as calm as you please, and the anchor came up as though it had been greased. "That fellow won't be troublin' another ship in quite a while," he went on. "I tied every one of his arms in a different kind o' sailor knot and he'll be untyin' 'em a long time."

Old Stormalong got sort of bored with sea-goin' after that voyage. He said no boat was big enough for him, and he bought an inland farm over between Pittsfield and Holyoke. Folks out that way say his farm was so rich that if you planted tenpenny nails in it at night they'd spring up crow bars in the morning. He had as fine a crop o' young Morgan colts as there was in the state and he got them all in three days' time just by plantin' horsehairs down on the south forty in the dark of the moon.

About that time Stormie got married, but his wife took to complaining about his drinkin' liquor made of equal parts of forked lightnin' and brimstone. He got pretty tired of hearin' her chatter, so one day he invented a steam wheelbarrow, set his wife in it, and away she went. He didn't hear from her for forty years, and then it was only her ghost flittin' around and tryin' to bother him. Stormie said he didn't mind *that* so long as she couldn't talk.

Old Stormalong got pretty homesick for the smells of the sea and the fo'c'sle before he'd been

on land very long. So he sold his farm and set out for the Massachusetts coast. He hit salt water just a bit to the north of Boston harbor and when he got there he could just hear a sailorman's chanty coming across the water from far out to sea. It was the crew of the *Courser*, the biggest boat in the universe—so big, in fact, that it couldn't get into Boston harbor. It had anchored way outside and was unloading a cargo onto regular-sized boats for them to bring in. No sooner did Old Stormie hear of it than he plunged into the waves and began swimming toward it.

Well, when Old Stormie climbed aboard hand over hand on the anchor chain, the captain took one look at him and said:

"It's Old Stormalong. You take the boat, Stormie. I'll rest a voyage home in the arms of my wife."

And so Stormie became captain of the *Courser*, and they put out to sea.

Now, the *Courser* was so big that she carried stables for hundreds of horses so that her men could ride their watches. Her masts were so tall they had to be hinged so that the top sections could be let down when the moon or the sun went by. Her sails were so big that the only flat place large enough for them to be made was the Sahara Desert. And she was so big all over that she had to stay out in one of the oceans because no harbor could hold her.

Her rigging featured four topsail yards on the bowsprit, with the halyards leading down through a groove in the keel, up through the stern windows, and hitched to the first mate's geranium box. Her windlass was satinwood inlaid with sea horses, and her galley was furnished with a Franklin County, galley-sliding, telescopic stovepipe made of hard rubber, and with a machine for making sea-foam taffy candy for the sailors. Besides her regular rigging, she flew a sail something like a kite called a "skyfungarorum," which is set in light weather about seventy-five feet above the main truck and made fast by a double-running hitch under the binnacle and aft, through the galley, to the cookstove.

When the *Courser* got to mid-ocean on that voyage she ran into the worst hurricane in the last hundred years. Twenty-seven men working at the wheel couldn't keep her on her course, and by the time the blow was over and Old Stormie had figured out her position by navigation she was in the North Sea and southbound. The *Courser* was too big to turn around in the North Sea and the only chance she had of getting back into free deep water was by running through the English Channel, and that looked too narrow to let her through.

"All hands over to soap the sides," yelled Old Stormalong. "Soap her extry heavy on the starboard."

Then Stormie took the wheel himself and eased her through. The Dover cliffs scraped off every bit of soap on the starboard side—that's why they've been so white and shining ever since—and the *Courser* lost a little paint, but she came through and Stormie let her run south for the Gulf of Mexico. It was while he was down there that he took sick from eatin' six sharks for breakfast and died from indigestion. The boys sewed him up in an extra mainsail and slipped him overboard.

They say the water raised three inches in those parts when he settled down to the bottom.

HOW ICHABOD PADDOCK PLAYED PINOCHLE IN A WHALE'S BELLY

The story of Ichabod Paddock and the bewitched whale is told in many ways. This is one of the nicest I have found in a search around Siasconset and Nantucket.

WHEN the Indian giant, Maushope, has caught a whale and roasted it in a fire made with trees which he has uprooted, the Indians of Nantucket Island say he devours his feast and then sits down to enjoy his pipe. They say it is the low-spreading smoke from that pipe which the white men in Nantucket call fog. And it is while Maushope smokes his pipe that the islanders, sitting comfortably beside their own fires with their own pipes in hand, swap yarns of other days —days when the whalers of Nantucket were a rich, proud lot, building pillared homes which still stand and are still occupied by the families who built them.

Comfortable folks, sitting out the fog, are likely to begin their session by getting into a laughing fit over an incident of comparatively recent occurrence—when Gasper Mano harpooned a swordfish and went on a long journey—a Nantucket sleigh ride, old whalers call it. The sleigh was Gasper's own dory and the steed a tremendous fish that tore through the water at nearly thirty miles an hour for enough hours to carry the astonished passenger into Canadian waters. There Canadian coast guard officials immediately arrested him for fishing in a prohibited locality. Luckily, Gasper Mano had an honest face and a convincing tongue, and the judge let him go.

Gasper Mano's adventure is sure to bring up at least one story about early Nantucket's most astonishing inhabitant, one Captain Ichabod Paddock who used to state emphatically that Nantucket whalers could outdo those of any other section and that he himself could prove it.

According to common custom, he would say, mainland whaling captains used to order the end of the lead soaped so that it would pick up grains of sand from the sea's bottom when soundings were taken. Then from the depth of the water and the looks of the sand they said they could pretty well tell where they were without shooting the sun or any other navigation figuring.

But Nantucket captains, Ichabod Paddock asserted, always tasted the end of the lead, and could tell by rolling the sand on their tongues just what part of the ocean's floor they were over.

Captain Ichabod Paddock's first mate was a mainlander who didn't take much stock in such wild statements, but one day Captain Ichabod felt his rheumatism coming on and stayed below in his cabin. When he ordered soundings taken he also told the first mate to have the lead soaped and, after it had been cast and pulled up, to bring it down to him to taste. The mate did this twice to the captain's satisfaction, but he was getting annoyed all the same by the captain's claim that he could tell where the boat was from the flavor of the bottom under it. So the third time the captain ordered the lead cast, the mate just heaved it down into the hold which was pretty well filled up with sand ballast from Nantucket Island. Then he yanked the lead back up and, with a sneer, took it down for Captain Ichabod to taste.

The captain hardly got his tongue on it before he leaped out of bed shouting:

"Jumping Jehoshaphat! We're wrecked right in the middle of my aunt Lizzie's garden!"

When Ichabod was a stout young captain and

engaged to as pretty and upstanding a Nantucket girl as there was on the whole island, he ran abaft a great bull whale less than a half day's sail out of Siasconset. Ordering the small boat lowered, Ichabod himself took the long dart and hurled it at the side of the great beast. It splintered into tenpenny nails. With harpoon after harpoon Ichabod tried to pierce the monster—but it was no use. Its hide was tougher than chain armor.

Now Ichabod was convinced that there was something devilish strange about that whale and that the toughness of its sides must indicate that they concealed something pretty valuable. So he yanked off his boots, dove overboard and began swimming around the whale. Again and again he circumnavigated the monster, which seemed for a while quite amused by the performance. But as Ichabod swam circle after circle, the whale finally got a little bored and he yawned.

This was the moment for which Ichabod had been waiting and, coming out of the water like a porpoise, he dove right down that whale's gullet. When he had made a landing on the banks of the whale's alimentary canal, and his eyes had got a little accustomed to the darkness, Ichabod groped his way around until he came to a long passageway which led toward a lighted window at the other end. He found a door beside the window, opened it, and went inside.

He found himself in as neatly fixed up a captain's cabin as he'd ever seen. There were beautiful maps on the walls and a rum cupboard twice as big as most. And seated on a big chair in front of it was a tall redheaded green-eyed girl who smiled at Ichabod and said:

"I've been waiting for you!"

Now, many a Nantucket salt has told me that Ichabod should have had sense enough to know that a woman, and particularly a young redheaded one with green eyes, is a Jonah for any craft, even if it's a tarnation big whale. But being inside the whale, Ichabod was somewhat in the position of the original Jonah himself, so he just sat down beside the girl and before long they were having a good talk and playing a cutthroat game of pinochle.

Ichabod had such a good time that he stayed pretty late, and he hated to go so much when he said good night that he said:

"How about tomorrow night?"

The redheaded green-eyed girl said she'd be pleased to have him drop in, she was sure.

And so the pinochle games got more and more numerous and Captain Ichabod's crew began to wonder where he went every evening when he took off his boots and jumped into the ocean and didn't return until way late in the night. And the girl Ichabod was engaged to began to notice he didn't come around any more, although his boat was layin' just a few miles off Siasconset. Her name was Patience, but as she often said, she got the name before her character developed.

After two Friday nights had gone by without her seeing anything of Ichabod, she began to get suspicions that were helped along a bit by the gossip the crew had set going around Nantucket and Siasconset. So one day she borrowed her father's dory and did a little cruising, arriving in the vicinity of the whale just in time to see Ichabod's big feet going down the monster's exposed throat.

Patience was thinking pretty hard by the time she got back home—and the first thing she said to her father in the morning was:

"Pa, would you be willing to lose great-grandma's silver tea set if you lost with it a great big overgrown girl like me who eats a lot and needs almost as much cloth as a mainsail to cover her?"

And her pa said:

"Well, daughter, if I was sure they'd get into good hands I could lose 'em both with considerable calm."

Folks that went by their house that morning saw a lot of smoke comin' out the chimney and said:

"Patience will spoil her baking with a fire as hot as that."

They'd have been mightily surprised if they had known that Patience was melting down her great-grandma's silver tea set in order to make a weapon to kill a witch with—although of course they all knew that it takes silver to pierce a witch's skin.

On the next day, Patience and her pa set out in the dory, the old man rowing and Patience in the bow with a shiny new harpoon in her hand. They hove to alongside the whale just a bit before sundown. The big fellow was just lyin' comfortable along the surface and waitin' for Ichabod to come along and amuse him until he got bored. He didn't pay any attention to a dory rowed by an old man and carryin' one girl passenger.

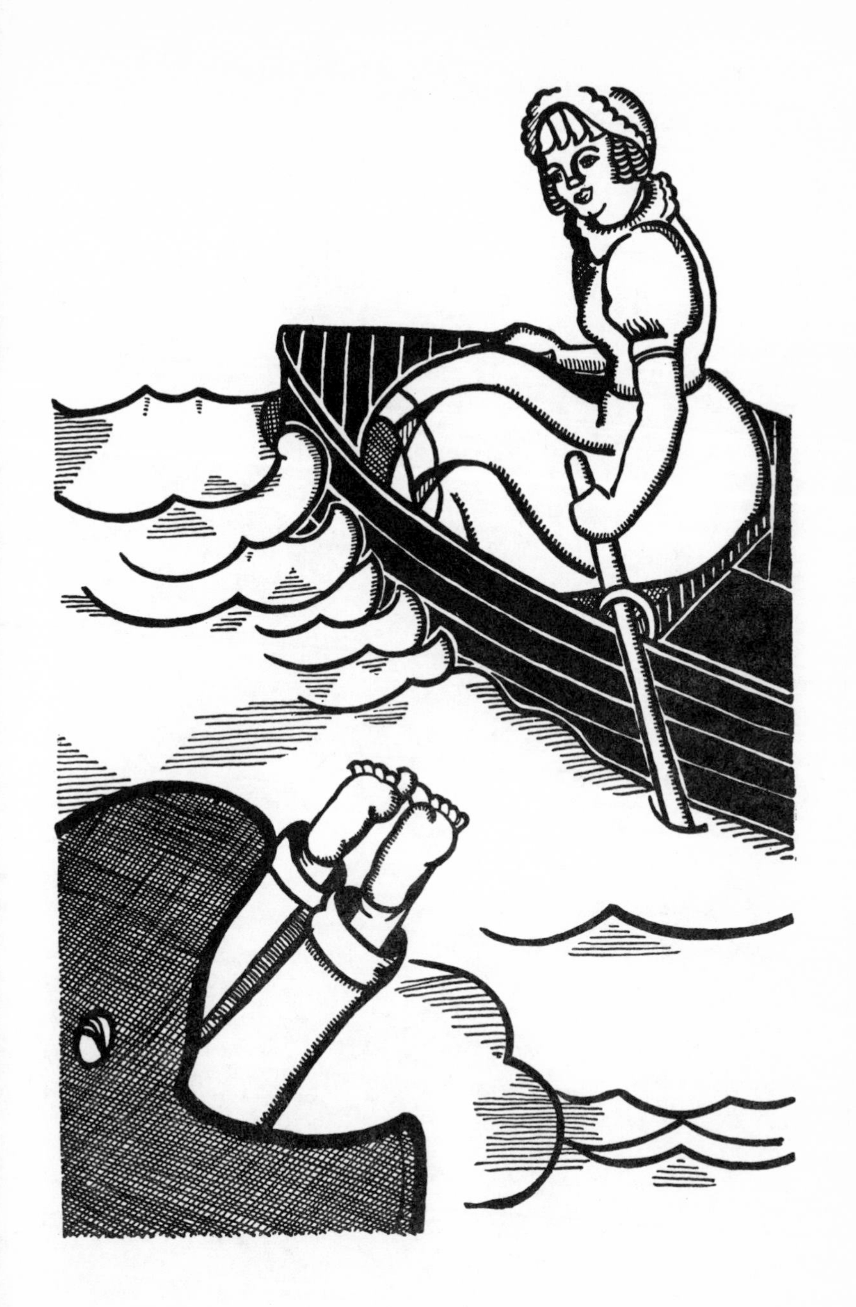

Just then Ichabod came swimming along and he looked mighty shamefaced when he saw Patience. He said he was jest out for a little swim after supper.

Patience said that was real nice but she'd like for him to get in the boat and sock her shiny new iron into that whale. So Ichabod climbed aboard. He knew the whale wouldn't mind, so he socked Patience's harpoon at him. By the Great Horn Spoon, the harpoon took! The whale began thrashing around, and first thing the three of them knew they were on a Nantucket sleigh ride that took them up to the Canadian border, south to New York harbor, and back to where they'd started from.

When the whale at last gave up the ghost they towed him in to Nantucket and cut him open. They got ten thousand dollars' worth of sperm oil out of him and a bit of greenish seaweed that had faded to a kind of red at one end.

After that, Patience and Ichabod got married, but Patience never told Ichabod that she had figured it out that the big whale was bewitched. She never told him what the shiny harpoon that had killed the whale had been made of. And whenever he asked her where her great-grandma's silver tea set was, she declared she must have put it aside somewhere and one of these days she must have a look for it.

CLAWING LEATHER

Away out yonder in Arizony where it ain't rained since Noah and it's so dry you have to prime yourself to spit thar's a wonderful forest whar the trees is a-growin' jest the same as they did centuries and centuries ago, but a-a-ll pewtrified, ladies and gentlemen, a-a-ll pewtrified. And the roots of them thar trees is a-growin' way down in the ground—a-spreadin' out and a-takin' holt on the dirt jest the same as they did centuries and centuries ago—but a-a-ll pewtrified, ladies and gentlemen, a-a-ll pewtrified; and the branches of them thar trees is a-growin' full of twigs and leaves and birds' nests jest the same as they did centuries and centuries ago. And flyin' around in them thar branches and through the pewtrified air is a number of pine hens, sandhill cranes, white-necked ravens, and yellow-headed blackbirds, all a-singin' their beautiful songs just as they did centuries and centuries ago but a-a-ll pewtrified, ladies and gentlemen, a-a-ll pewtrified.

Now when I give a lecture on Arizony up to Boston last week and told this interestin' scientific fact, some unbelievin' miscreant sings out, "What about the law of gravitation?" and I sings right back at him, "Seems to me anybody with the sense of a coyote'd know that way out there in Arizony this here now law of gravitation hain't worked for centuries and centuries but is like everythin' else aout there—a-a-ll pewtrified, ladies and gentlemen, completely pewtrified.

HOW PECOS BILL WON AND LOST HIS BOUNCING BRIDE

Most of the Westerners who tell stories about the greatest cowboy of them all, Pecos Bill, agree that he came from the banks of the Pecos River not far from Elvira, New Mexico. I heard his story from an Arizona cowboy who said Pecos must have left New Mexico early to get so well known around Arizona in places like Bumble Bee and Silver Bell, Skull Valley and Burnt Ranch, Wolf Hole and Wide Ruins. Texas cow hands know Pecos Bill, too.

THE story Arizona cowboys like most to tell when they've finished their day's ride, emptied the chuck wagon, and are seated in the flickering light of the campfire, is the tale of Pecos

Bill. Every time somebody or other tells about Bill the story gets longer. If you were to listen tonight along the banks of the Turkey River or the Blue, you'd be pretty sure to hear some buckaroo telling about how Pecos Bill licked a mountain lion barehanded, jumped astride his back and rode him into camp, using a rattlesnake he had picked up along the way as a quirt. And some broncobuster from over Chloride way or maybe from Diversion or Sandwater may be telling about the perpetual motion ranch. And after that one's been told, somebody will start up one of the songs that Pecos Bill made up while he was riding the range, *The Chisholm Trail* maybe, or *The Trail to Mexico*, or maybe *The Strawberry Roan.*

Pecos Bill thought he was a coyote until he was almost a grown man. When he was a little boy he had fallen off the end of the big wagon in which he and his sixteen brothers and sisters were being carried westward in a wagon train. When Bill's parents counted noses that night, they realized their loss and tried to find him on the back trail, but they never did. For Bill had been taken up by the coyotes and they had asked him to go home with them. The coyotes taught Bill to sit and howl at the moon just as they did and he soon

forgot about being a human being. It wasn't until Bill was eighteen that he realized he wasn't a real coyote. Then he met a cowboy who said:

"Well, if you're a coyote, where's your tail?"

That convinced Bill, and so he left his four-footed friends and went to live in an Arizona town.

One day Bill was riding along beside the Salt River when he saw a pretty girl riding towards him on the back of a rearing, bucking, plunging catfish. Although it was a small catfish for the Salt, hardly larger than a whale, Bill was so pleased at the way the girl handled it with only a surcingle for harness that he fell in love with her and asked her to marry him.

She said her name was Sue and she would be pleased to marry him if he would grant her two requests. Bill was so in love with her he said "yes" before asking what they were.

The first thing she asked for was a bustle to wear on her wedding day. Now, a bustle was a very fashionable article of wearing apparel in the time she asked for it. Every fine lady wore one under her skirt just below her waist in the back and hoped it would give her a big curve just at the place where ladies now hope they have no curves at all. Bill bought Sue the finest bustle in the country—made of steel wire and whalebone—and they were both very happy over it.

But Bill was troubled about Sue's second request. She wished to ride Bill's horse, Widow-Maker, on her wedding day. Though she could ride a bucking catfish, Bill doubted if she could ride Widow-Maker. Still, he had promised, and so after the wedding ceremony he let her get on the horse and start to ride.

Widow-Maker was not accustomed to skirts about his ribs and he bucked so hard that Sue fell off and landed on the bustle—and bounced. The first bounce took her over the lower horn of the new moon. When she came back down that bustle hit on the Rocky Mountains and bounced her back into the sky and completely over the moon.

Bill kept begging her not to be so nervous and he tried mighty hard to figure out some way of stopping her bouncing, but he has never been able to. She is still bouncing out there, and every once in a while on a clear night Arizonians can see her pass across the face of the moon.

When he found out he could never claim his bride, Bill sat down and began to cry. He is still crying, and it is his flowing tears that made the river that Arizona folks call the Silver.

HOW KEMP MORGAN GREASED THE SKY

The boss of all the oil drillers has always been Kemp Morgan. Kemp started all the booms they ever had out in Oklahoma. No wonder they like to talk about him in Jet and Lone Wolf, Frogville and Okay, Rotary and Bushyhead.

IN the old days in the southwestern states folks used to try to find oil beneath the ground just as they used to try to find water. With a forked stick of hazelwood held in both hands in front of him, the waterfinder would walk over the earth until the stick suddenly bent downward. Then he would tell the man who owned the land to dig his well right there if he wanted to be sure to strike water. The oilfinders sometimes used a forked stick made of different wood—of willow, maybe, or peach—and they didn't have good luck all the time. Sometimes the landowners dug holes very deep into the earth without finding any oil. They called those holes dusters and they would get pretty mad when they had dug for a long time only to find out they had been working on a duster.

But all those hard times and uncertainties were before Kemp Morgan showed up. Kemp's sense of smell was so sharp that all he had to do to find the oil beneath the ground was to sniff real hard. If he smelled oil, the oil was there below, and no two ways about it. Kemp Morgan was the greatest oil-well driller of all time. After he had sniffed oil he'd take a spade and dig down to where solid rock began and he'd hit that rock in just a few minutes. Then he'd set up his steel drill and start it to work whacking a hole down through the rock. When he hit into oil it would spurt up through the hole in a great gusher and Kemp would have to work fast to enclose it in a casing and get it to running off into barrels. Such work usually takes a large crew all working at once—but Kemp wasn't very sociable and he preferred to work alone. He was so big and so fast that he could build the high tower of an oil derrick in less than an hour.

Of course, he sometimes made mistakes. There was the summer he lost his best drill when it got below the rock surface into a starch mine. It kept going slower as it got more and more stuck up, and when the starch finally set even Kemp couldn't move the drill either way.

Kemp was just as smart as he was strong. One cold night when his drill hit into oil the gusher sent oil high in the air where it froze in one huge pillar. Kemp immediately got his ax and cut it up into pieces as long as a railroad car and shipped it to market on flat cars to save himself the high rent on tank cars.

Another time Kemp had got a hole dug down about a mile when a wind came up and blew all the dirt from around that hole and left it sticking a mile up in the air. Kemp got a saw and cut that hole up into four-foot lengths. Then he split each one in half with his ax and that made them just the right size for post holes. He shipped the whole lot of them over to Kansas where the dirt is so hard it takes a farmer about a year to dig up a potato. The Kansas farmers bought Kemp's postholes and sent him word it was a sight easier driving those ready-made postholes down into Kansas dirt than it was trying to dig a hole out of it.

The biggest oil derrick in the history of the world was raised by Kemp Morgan. One time he sniffed the largest oil supply ever tapped down below the surface of Oklahoma. So he dug and he dug but he didn't seem to hit oil. A friend came by and laughed and said:

"I guess this time you've dug just a duster, after all. I guess you can't sniff as well as you used to."

"Smell's getting stronger all the time," said Kemp and kept on digging.

After he'd got down about ten miles, the friend came back and said:

"You'd better give up, Kemp. You've got a duster this time, sure enough."

"She's just about to come in," said Kemp, and he built his derrick so high that it had to be hinged on two different sides to let the moon and the sun go by. Just as he finished it—Whoosh! the oil shot up out of that ten-mile hole so high that no one could see the top of it. It happened to be a cloudy day and the first thing anybody knew that oil had greased all the clouds so that they began to slip and slide around through the air. First they'd all be on one side of the sky, and then they'd all begin slipping to the other side. Finally they all ended up in a heap right in the middle and the collision started them raining oil. It rained oil for a week all over Oklahoma so hard that all

the folks who had dug dusters found they had been filled with oil and all the oil drillers in the state were happy, just as Kemp Morgan wanted them to be.

HOW STRAP BUCKNER FOUGHT THE FOUL FIEND

The cowboys of Texas have elected Strap Buckner their patron saint. In Bald Prairie, Eulogy, Desdemona, Samson, or Pointblank there will surely be an old-timer to tell this wild poetic story.

TEXAS is so big and folks there tell so many good stories that it is embarrassing to try to pick out one that is better than the rest. Since Texans as a whole are independent, ambitious people, I have decided that their story about Strap Buckner is best suited to them.

Strap was one of the first of three hundred colonists that Stephen Austin brought to San Felipe in Texas. He had good reason for feeling independent, for he was a giant among men—and he had the strength of a giant. Folks who knew him said that while Samson, according to the Bible, was the strongest man of his time, having killed a lion singlehanded, Strap if he got the chance could play the same trick on ten lions at once. His hair was redder than a campfire and it looked like one except for being bigger, and his face was a meadow of blooming freckles.

Strap was a good-natured fellow, but he had a peculiar kind of talent that weighed on him. That was a genius for knocking men down. He hardly ever knocked anybody down because he was angry. He did it because it was one thing he could do better than anybody else, and he felt called upon to contribute that to the community. At one time or another he knocked down no less than three times every one of the three hundred colonists, not sparing the boss, Stephen Austin, himself.

He had just got started on the male Indian population of Texas when he got a chance to exercise his gift on a more difficult subject. A great black bull called Noche had been scaring folks around there out of their wits, and things had come to such a pass that it was as much as life was worth to go outdoors when Noche was about. Strap was very glad to find out that his talent might prove useful as well as entertaining, and sent Noche a challenge, which the bull accepted.

On the day appointed, Strap threw a red blanket over his shoulder just to make the bull madder and stepped out on the prairie while all the folks in the place looked on anxiously from their windows and roofs. Noche was waiting for him, and when he saw the red blanket he pawed the earth and let out a thundering bellow. Then Strap politely pawed the earth with his right foot and bellowed back. Such mocking was too much for Noche's temper and he charged at Strap like a great black thunderbolt. Strap met him halfway with a blow from his giant fist right on the bull's forehead. Noche's nose bled a mighty stream and he turned tail and ran away, bellowing weakly, and he was never seen again.

After that Strap went back to his ordinary daily round of knocking down Indians, but he did not have as much taste for it as before. He began throwing an iron pestle, the kind Texans used to grind grain with, at wildcats and bears and buffalo. He always killed his victims with one throw, but the animals around were soon wise enough to leave the region. Strap became unpopular after that because he had driven the game animals out of the neighborhood—and besides, the Indians and his white companions were getting tired of being knocked down and didn't take it as good-naturedly as they had in the past.

Strap was such a good-natured fellow that he couldn't bear to see his neighbors unhappy—and so he decided to leave San Felipe and go to some place where the wild animals didn't know about his deadly iron pestle and where being knocked down would be a new experience to the men who lived there. He cried a little when he said good-bye to his old friends and then he set out straight across Austin County into Fayette County and there on a branch of the Colorado River near what is now the town of La Grange he found a trading post run by Bob Turket and Bill Smotherall. Strap had let his one talent rust for so long, and he was so glad to see Bob and Bill, that he knocked them both down right off. When they got up they both said Strap had a great genius for knocking people down and welcomed him to the region.

Strap liked the country and built himself a cabin there and started right in where he had left off, knocking down Indians. In a week's time he had knocked down every male Indian within ten miles of his cabin. The Indians on the Colorado River were not so used to it as those around San Felipe and they seemed to enjoy it. The king of the Indians admired Strap greatly and gave him the name Kokublothetop-off, which in Indian language means Red Son of Blue Thunder. The king also gave him a gray bobtailed mustang which he said was the swiftest horse in the world, and he offered Strap his daughter, the Princess Tulipita, in marriage. Strap took the horse but he turned down the girl. He said he didn't think a genius should marry but should devote all his time to doing what he had a genius for.

Then one morning, when Strap got up, he found all the Indians had left. They had got tired of being knocked down—like the Indians around San Felipe—and had stolen away in the night. Strap felt mighty bad about that and cried and finally took a drink of fermented cactus juice out of a jug. Then he felt better and decided that the Indians were pretty poor stuff to exercise his genius on. He took another swallow and cried because he had never had a real chance to show how great his genius was. That gave him an idea. He took still another swallow and began to feel better, and then he began to howl something like this:

I'm wild and woolly
And full of fleas,

Ain't never been curried
Below the knees;
I'm a wild she-wolf
From Bitter Creek,
And it's my time
To h-o-w-l, whoopp-i-ee!

Howling like that made Strap feel so much better that he began to work on his new idea. He began to shout that he could knock down anybody in the world—or out of it—and if the Foul Fiend would give him a chance he'd beat the stuffing out of him. He got so excited that he said it three times, and just as he finished the third time there was a crack of thunder and right in front of him stood a strange figure with two red horns growing out of the forehead of a face like an eagle's. It had a long pointed tail, and feet that were notched in the middle. The figure opened its mouth and told Strap to meet it on a knoll beside the river the next morning at nine. Then it vanished, leaving a smell of brimstone behind.

The next morning at nine Strap met the weird creature at the foot of the knoll. It was now in the shape of an ugly dwarf, but while walking beside Strap on the way to the top of the knoll it changed, first to a black cat, then to a black bear, and finally into the figure Strap had seen the day before. Then, when they had arrived at the top of the knoll, it began to swell up. It got bigger and bigger until it was a hundred and ninety feet tall and eighty feet around, with its tail swelled up in proportion. Then it tossed the end of its tail into the air where it caught in a fork of a black cloud. It said to Strap: "If you will throw away your iron pestle, I will make myself smaller until I am just your size."

Strap threw the pestle away and the figure became his size. And then, just as they were about to begin to fight, the dark cloud in which the long tail was hooked began to float away, dragging the squealing figure with it. But it took the figure only a minute or so to roll itself up in the coil of its tail to the end and unhook it from the cloud. Then it descended to the knoll and the battle began.

That fight lasted all day long. The noise of it was so great that most of the Indians hid in caves under the earth, though about forty of the bravest of them stayed on the riverbank with Bob Turket and Bill Smotherall and listened.

Try as he might, using his tail and his split hooves as well as his fists, the Foul Fiend could not get the best of Strap Buckner. First one would go down and then the other as they struck each other with the force of lightning. Finally, just at the end of the day, the figure broke its word. It swelled up again to the height of a hundred and ninety feet, grabbed Strap and threw him across the back of a tremendous gray horse. Then, taking the form of a monkey, it leaped astride the horse and tore across the sky, with Strap hanging limp in front of it. The next day Bob Turket and Bill Smotherall with eleven hundred Indians visited the place of the fight. Rocks and trees and the land had been torn up in a circle of many miles' radius, and to this day that section near the Colorado River remains waste and desolate.

Three months later, Bob Turket and Bill Smotherall saw Strap Buckner riding his gray horse by their trading post. He didn't say anything, just rode on quietly with his head down as if he were looking for something. Bob and Bill and all the Indians were too frightened to make any noise, except for the Indian medicine man who made weird sounds on his big bongaroo drum.

That night Bob and Bill and ninety Indians who were watching with them saw a strange blue light over Strap Buckner's cabin and appearing out of it suddenly a huge gray horse galloping across the sky. On his back was a big man with long red hair that streamed out behind him. He was waving an iron pestle in his hand, threatening with it a monkey that rode in front of him and looked beaten and practically scared to death.

Texas folks say that Strap still rides the western skies on stormy nights when the lightning cracks and splits the sky in fancy patterns and the thunder growls and roars. They say they have seen his red hair flying out on the wind and the iron pestle lifted high in his right hand as the gray bobtailed mustang streaks across the top of the world.

HOW THE WHITE MUSTANG GAVE A LITTLE GIRL A PARTY

The whole of the wild West was the range of the White Mustang. The Indians have as many stories about him as the cavalry and the cow hands. In Wyoming, fathers and mothers who live in Lost Cabin, Sublet, Ten Sleep, and Wind River like to tell their children this story.

IN every western state where the prairie lands are level as far as any eye can see, there are stories of the wild white mustang. From the days when the Kiowa Indians first saw him and called him the Ghost Horse of the Prairies until today, every western rider has dreamed of catching and taming him and riding him at a great rodeo while all the West gasps in wonder and envy.

But folks who claim to know say that the white mustang will never be caught because he is not a real horse of flesh and blood. They point out that he never grows old—that rifle bullets pass right through him without hurting him or even slowing his great speed—that no matter how far he is pursued he never tires. Cowboys who have chased him say the wild white mustang is the most beautiful animal in the world—and the fastest. Although he has been chased countless times by clever riders on their fastest horses he has never yet been forced to break into a gallop. In a beautiful rocking pace, his two left feet off the ground at the same time, then the two right, he measures off mile after mile, leaving his desperately galloping pursuers far behind.

There are many stories about the phantom wild horse. Once when I lived at Fort Sill on the Oklahoma plains a cowboy told me that in the old days folks around there made a great plan to capture the beast. They had lured him into a big circular valley—and they figured that by chasing him round and round it, using a fresh horse and rider at the end of every mile, they must finally tire out their prey and catch him. So they brought a hundred of the fastest horses in Oklahoma into the valley, and a hundred of the best cowboy riders, and started the chase. All day and all night they pursued the ghost horse—and at the end of every mile a new rider and a fresh steed took out after him. The white pacer never seemed to change his speed, but no cowboy got close enough to him to throw his lasso at him in all of a hundred miles. At the end of the long chase the white horse climbed a high cliff at the edge of the valley and neighed a wild cry of triumph over his foes before he turned and tirelessly paced away.

The best of all the stories about the white mustang is the one about how he took little Gretchen to a party. Gretchen's parents had packed all their belongings in a covered wagon when they started westward and they had packed their three little girls in on top of all the furniture and bedding. By the time they had got into Texas, Gretchen, who was the youngest and liveliest, had become very tired of being bumped along in such a little space—and so she asked to be allowed to ride the old mare that followed the wagon carrying on her back two big sacks of corn meal. At first her parents refused—but they finally tied Gretchen on the mare's back between the meal sacks. There she was very happy watching the glistening waters of the Guadeloupe River, as the wagon rolled along its banks, and the drifting clouds that threw big shadows down on the wide, level Texas land.

Late in the afternoon the wagon in front of Gretchen got stuck in the mud beside the river and the mare she was riding wandered off a short distance to graze. The afternoon had been so hot and the day so long that Gretchen fell asleep. The next thing she knew she was awakened by feeling the horse beneath her stretching out to a full gallop. Then she saw that the mare was following a big white mustang that neighed in a persuasive and inviting manner and looked back anxiously as it passed along. Although she was frightened, Gretchen realized that she was tied on too securely to fall off and she began to enjoy flying along so swiftly. After she had ridden many miles, the white horse turned into a little green valley and many other horses rushed up to greet him. They looked with wonder at the little girl on the mare's back and they sniffed at the meal bags. They smelled the good corn inside and began to nip at the ropes that held the bags in place. Gretchen tried to untie the knots about her legs that her father had made to keep her from falling but she could not reach them and the hungry horses could not help nipping close to her feet. She was frightened and began to cry.

At that moment the white horse moved in

close to her and drove the other horses away. Then he carefully bit in two the ropes that held Gretchen, got a good hold with his teeth on the back of her dress, lifted her off the mare and set her gently down beneath a bush that grew beside a water hole near by. Then he brought the meal bags and set them down in front of her and she took a handful and ate it. At that all the hungry horses came up and ate some of the meal and Gretchen drank some water from the water hole and then the horses drank too, and Gretchen laughed because she was enjoying the white mustang's cornmeal party a great deal. All the horses stayed quite late, but when the valley began to get dark and stars came out above it, they wandered off, and Gretchen curled herself up and slept happily under the bush.

When the rays of the sun woke her in the morning, however, she was lonesome and wanted to see her parents. The old mare came and stood beside her, but Gretchen was much too short to be able to get on her back. After she had tried to climb up again and again she began to cry. The white mustang heard her and raced over to her side. Again he picked her up by the back of her dress and this time he set her down on the mare's back. Then he started out very fast, with the mare following him, out of the valley and across the wide plain. It was not long before Gretchen, who was having a hard time staying where she had been put without being tied on, saw the white top of her father's covered wagon.

The mare carried her on into the camp her father had made while he searched for his little lost daughter, but the white mustang stayed just in sight and watched. When he saw that Gretchen was safe in her mother's arms and her father was bending over her in great joy for her return, the white mustang turned and began to pace away so fast that he looked like a white streak. His flowing snow-white mane and his long snow-white tail looked like wings skimming along the ground.

THE DIMPLE ON THE CHEEK OF THE GODDESS OF LIBERTY

For as unto the crown the jewels are, so unto the Nation is Dixie. She is the red and white of the American flag, and some of the blue. She is the dimple on the cheek of the Goddess of Liberty. . . . She is the diamond pin on the shirt bosom of Yankee Doodle. The sun rises on Yankee Doodle and sets on the West, but he is at the full meridian of his glory Away Down South in Dixie.

—GOVERNOR ROBERT LOVE TAYLOR *of Tennessee.*

HOW TONY BEAVER BUILT THE CANDY DAM

West Virginia lumberjacks like to tell the stories about Tony Beaver. Sometimes Tony gets mixed up in an adventure with a smart character from the southern part of the state whose name is Brer Rabbit. Here are some reports from Hawk's Nest and Pruntytown and Four Pole Junction.

IN the high West Virginia mountains where the Eel River dashes down toward what mountain folks call "The Levels" is the lumber camp of Tony Beaver. It's pretty hard to find because, in the first place, not even the best map of West Virginia shows the course of Eel River and, in the second place, the camp is so deep in the woods. But if you want to find it very much and if you set out into the mountains and use your imagination enough, you will get there. And before long you will be in a big cook-tent beside Eel River and Tony Beaver will be saying:

"How about a second piece of this apple

pie made out of genuine West Virginia Golden Delicious apples?"

There are a lot of folks in West Virginia who can tell a good many Tony Beaver stories without repeating themselves. In towns like Black Betsey and Jumping Branch and Sleepy Creek the tale of Tony and the West Virginia buckwheat pancakes is still going strong.

Tony went to visit his grandma once and she baked him some mighty fine buckwheat cakes. Granny's griddle was as big as a whole township and when she got it good and hot she bound big sides of bacon on Tony's feet and let him go skating on it to grease it. Tony ate a hundred cakes that day before he started in using syrup and after that he ate a couple hundred more *with* syrup.

Then Tony said he guessed he wasn't very hungry today and asked his grandma if she'd mind very much if he wrapped up the rest of the cakes she'd made and took them home. Grandma said, of course he could take them along, and so Tony wrapped up the pancakes and started out.

He was just passing through a stretch of woods when he ran slap into that smart Brer Rabbit who is such a famous character all over

West Virginia and the rest of the South. Brer Rabbit said:

"I see you're totin' some of your grandma's buckwheat cakes. Now I got quite a few persimmons in this big package *and* I've got a good idea. We'll just lay your pancakes and my persimmons out on a log—first a pancake and then a persimmon—and then I'll say a few spell words over them that will make them turn into just twice as many and we can have a feast."

Tony's walk had already made him hungry and so he agreed to follow out Brer Rabbit's idea. He began laying cakes on a fallen log and Brer Rabbit began laying persimmons beside them. While they were at it Brer Rabbit recited this rhyme:

First a persimmon—then a cake;
Don't let me get a belly-ache.

When all the cakes and persimmons were laid out on the log, Brer Rabbit all of a sudden hollered out, "Bingo!"—grabbed up all the cakes and persimmons and started to run off with them! But Tony Beaver was too quick for him. Brer Rabbit was in the air on his first hop when Tony Beaver fetched him a lick that knocked him higher than a kite. The wind caught his big ears as if they were sails and away Brer Rabbit went, sailing around all over West Virginia for seven days, dropping persimmons and pancakes all the while he was up there. All the boys and girls in the state got out baskets and barrels to catch them, and to this day folks talk about the week it rained pancakes and persimmons on West Virginia.

Tony Beaver had a yoke of oxen that could pull almost anything into the middle of next week. Each ox had a pair of horns with so much spread that it would take a jay bird six years to fly from the tip of one horn to the tip of the other. Tony never found anything his oxen couldn't pull to market except one of his especially grown West Virginia watermelons. The melons on Tony's patch grew so big that even the smallest one wouldn't fit into the biggest wagon. So Tony wound a little one with ropes and spliced the ropes to the ox harness. The oxen got the melon started all right, but when they got near Eel River the traces broke and the melon rolled right down into the river and hit bottom so hard it busted. Tony and his gang of lumberjacks jumped onto the seeds as they came to the

surface and began yelling and singing and spinning the seeds with their feet, and they put on the biggest drive ever seen on Eel River. When they got down to the sawmill dam they sold their drive as peeled logs and some of the finest houses in West Virginia are made out of planks from those very watermelon seeds.

Perhaps the best of all the stories about Tony Beaver is the one that tells how he built the candy dam. There had been an uncommonly wet fall in West Virginia one year and Eel River had begun to rise above its banks. It got higher and higher and pretty soon the little town near Tony's camp was in danger of being flooded and carried downstream. Nobody seemed to know what to do until a little schoolboy said to his companions:

"Let's go tell Tony Beaver about it. He can do anything."

So they started out to go to Tony's camp and they got lost in the woods and would have wandered around for days if Tony Beaver had not heard they were coming and sent one of his loggers out to find them. He found them all right and a little while after that they were in the big cook-tent of Tony's camp and Tony was saying:

"How about a second piece of that Golden Delicious apple pie?"

The children told Tony how high the river was getting and how they and their parents were in danger of being drowned. So Tony called to his men and they all jumped on saw logs and rode them through the swift waters down the Eel River to the town, each lumberjack carrying one of the children back home. Then Tony took command.

"Open up your molasses warehouses," he told the men of the town, "and bring me every barrel of molasses you've got. And open up all your storage houses and bring me every bag of West Virginia peanuts you can find!"

The men did what he told them to and Tony said to his crew of lumberjacks:

"Roll those barrels up the river six miles to Blacksmith's Bend and the rest of you folks drag along those bags of peanuts."

When everybody got to Blacksmith's Bend, Tony said to his men:

"Knock in the heads of those barrels and pour the molasses in the river—and the rest of you folks start shucking peanuts and throwing them in."

So everybody was as busy as a beaver for a long time and finally all the molasses and all the peanuts were in the river.

"Jee-ru-salem!" shouted Tony Beaver. "I nearly forgot something," and he dashed back to his camp and came running back waving a vinegar cruet as big as a cider factory and a salt shaker as big as the Capitol Building in Washington. He emptied the vinegar and the salt in the stream and then he said:

"Let's follow this mess downstream and see what happens."

The sun came out about then and the whole crowd walking downstream saw the river begin to thicken up. As the sun got hotter and hotter the river got thicker and thicker and slower and slower. Just before they got to town the flow stopped altogether and the river began to pile up a shiny, brownish dam full of big white particles. It got bigger and bigger until it protected the town completely. There was no more danger of flood now.

"Break off a piece of the dam and taste it," said Tony to the schoolboy who had thought of telling him of the danger. So the schoolboy bit off a piece and tasted it.

"It's peanut brittle!" he cried. And so it was—and all the children of the town had all the peanut brittle they wanted all winter as a result of Tony Beaver's building the candy dam.

HOW ANNIE CHRISTMAS MOURNED FOR HER GAMBLING MAN

Annie Christmas was a sure-enough New Orleans product. They understand about her in places like Big Africa, Cash Point, Vermilion Bayou, and Hell Hole, but her real hangouts were Tchoupitoulas Street and Jackson Square and the river docks along the edges of the French Quarter in New Orleans.

ALONG the colorful water front of New Orleans, and up the river even as far as Natchez, Mississippi, folks talk a great deal about a strange woman. Though they say she's been dead for some time, rivermen still measure strength by her standards.

He's almost as strong as Annie Christmas," they say about men who have done superhuman things.

For Annie Christmas weighed two hundred and fifty pounds, stood six-foot-eight barefooted, wore the largest and most beautifully curled mustache along the entire river, and was more powerful than any riverman who ever lived.

Annie Christmas could carry three barrels of flour at once, one balanced on her head and one under each arm. When the river got high one spring and was about to flood the country above New Orleans, Annie Christmas prevented the disaster by throwing up a new and higher levee all by herself in one day.

One time she wanted to get a loaded flatboat from New Orleans up the river to Natchez in a hurry—so she just grabbed the towline and set out on a dead run. They say the bottom of that flatboat scarcely touched the water on the entire trip. The captain just leaned back in his chair and tried to make his fiddle sound like a mockin'bird, and the crew amused themselves by making bets with the river gulls about who would get to the next bend the quickest.

Annie Christmas was a great fighter, too. When she knew she was going to have a fight, she dressed in men's clothes and trimmed her long curling mustache close, so that it wouldn't offer anybody a good hold. She licked the daylights out of every bully on the lower river and, they say, Mike Fink, the champion fighter of the Ohio Valley, never came to New Orleans again after she sent him word that if he showed up in Louisiana once more she would have him poled back up the river lashed to the keel of his keelboat.

Annie wore a bead necklace when she was all dressed up and looking pretty. It had a bead in it for every ear or nose she'd chawed off and every eye she'd gouged out in her fights. When she died it was thirty feet long.

Annie had just one weakness—a gamblin' man named Charlie. Charlie had a curvin' mustache that was even longer and shinier than Annie's, and he wore waistcoats that would put your eye out. Annie was in love with Charlie for a long time before he'd have anything to do with her, but he finally gave in and married her, and the next year she presented him with twelve sons all at once, and before they were six years old every one of them was over seven feet tall.

One night Charlie went to a gambling hall in New Orleans—on Tchoupitoulas Street—and began to play roulette. He put a quarter on red, leaned his head on his hand, and watched the little ball finally come to rest. Red won. Charlie never moved—just let his money ride. Red won again, and again. After it had won five times straight, Charlie's friends begged him to stop while he was so far ahead. He was bound to lose sooner or later, they said. But Charlie paid no attention—just sat there with his head on his hand and not moving a muscle. When red had won for the sixteenth time and Charlie was over eight thousand dollars ahead, the croupier announced that the house would not play with him any longer and ordered him to leave. Charlie didn't move. The croupier pushed him and Charlie fell out of his chair to the floor. He had been dead for some time. The house had been playing against a dead man—and the dead man had won.

When Annie Christmas found out that Charlie was dead she was inconsolable. She gave him a very grand funeral and spent most of the eight thousand Charlie had won on it. Then she put on her thirty-foot necklace, her black silk dress, gave instructions to her twelve sons, and shot herself. The sons did what their mother told them to. They put their mother's body in a coal-black coffin and loaded it in a coal-black hearse drawn by sixteen coal-black horses. Then, six on each side, clothed in coal-black suits, they walked beside the hearse as the horses slowly rolled it down to the river. A coal-black barge

waited there and they put the coffin on it. At midnight, in the dark of the moon, they cut the coal-black moorings and Annie Christmas with six seven-foot sons on either side of her drifted down the river and out to sea, never to be seen again. And as they floated downstream between the levees, folks living near the river heard a strange mournful tune rising in the air. The tallest of her sons was singing a last song for Annie Christmas.

HOW JIM HIGGINS AND THE B'AR BEAT THE STEAMBOAT

Tennessee claims Jim Higgins, hero of the adventure of the Mysterious Pilot. Folks around Reelfoot, Golddust, Plum Point, and Reverie are still talking about his famous ride. Americans have always liked to tell bear stories. Jim's will stand up with the rest.

JIM HIGGINS had walked fifteen hundred miles up the river in six days and got started down again with a cargo when his flatboat ran aground on a sandbank. So Jim went huntin', for amusement, and in no time he had treed one of the biggest bears ever seen in the river country. Jim shook that bear down and started right in wrestlin' with him. After a hard fight he captured the bear alive, brought him on board, and tied him up to the anchor cable. Then he got out his old fiddle and began to play on it and give the bear lessons in how to dance. The animal was gettin' along pretty well when Jim heard a big noise and looked up the river to see the first steamboat that ever fluttered a wheel on the Mississippi bearin'

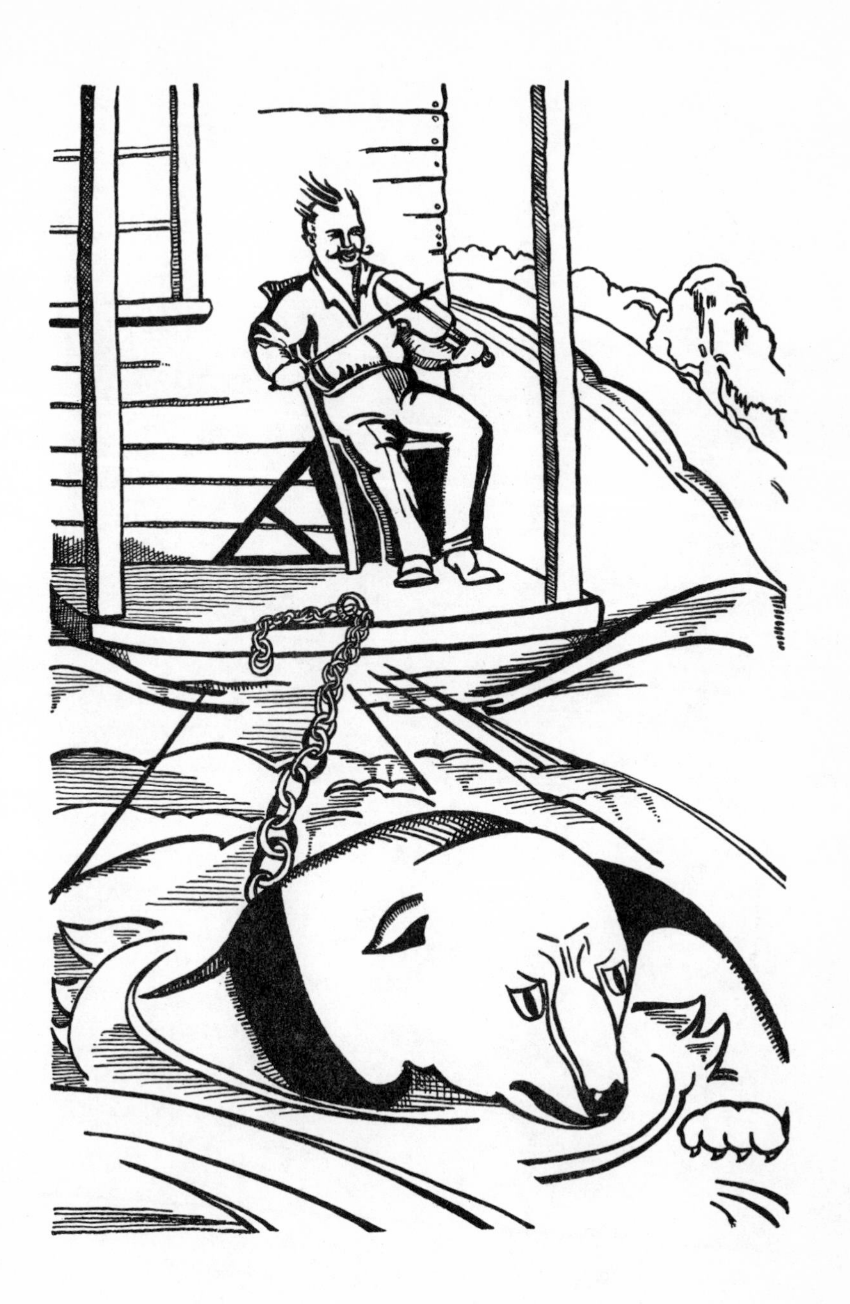

down on him. She was driving every fish and alligator in the river before her.

The bear took fright at the sight and jumped overboard. All of a sudden the flatboat jerked loose from the sand bar and took out after that steamboat. In a half hour it had caught up. For a while it was neck and neck, and then the flatboat began to draw ahead. She was ridin' like a dancin' feather and throwin' water from one bank to the other. The steamboat was doing the best it could but Jim's flatboat was doing better. Jim didn't know what was the matter but he was gettin' down to New Orleans fast, so he just sat back and fiddled away on tunes like *Rats in the Meal Barrel* and *All My Candy's Gone* and *Josephus on the Blossom.*

"It was the purtiest weather in the world," said Jim, "and I enjoyed it amazin'ly."

The speed of the floatboat made a breeze that kept him cool and the moon would peep down from the clouds once in a while. Before the night was over the boat had run up on the levee at New Orleans, beatin' the steamboat by a day and a half, and then Jim found out what made his craft go so fast.

When the bear had jumped overboard he

was still tied to the cable. A thunderin' big catfish had taken out after him the moment he hit the water and that bear had been so scared of being swallowed by the catfish he just lit out for New Orleans as fast as he could go.

He beat that fish by about six foot and a half. Nobody knows just how fast he pulled the boat, but the fish swam so fast that when he hit the levee he jumped fifty-seven feet out on land and folks say he didn't stop floppin' his tail for a month.

HOW RAILROAD BILL CHASED HIMSELF TO HIS GIRL'S HOME

Railroad Bill has been a popular fellow among the little cabins in the dark Alabama pines for a long time. At Saint Elmo, Sunny South, Verbena, and Vinegar Bend, if you listen hard, you can hear a whispering about him.

WHITE folks say Railroad Bill's real name was Morris Slater. But black boys and girls who tell stories and sing songs about him have never known him by any other name than Railroad Bill. Whatever his name was, he lived and still lives, they say, in the Alabama woods near the roadbed of the Louisville and Nashville Railroad. Sometimes when a poor old black woman wakes up in the morning and opens the door of her cabin she finds a neat little pile of canned goods on the step. There may be a couple of cans of soup, a can of snap beans, perhaps some black-eyed peas.

"God bless Railroad Bill," says the old woman, and she hurries to put the cans out of sight. She knows that Railroad Bill has taken those cans from a freight car on the L. & N. tracks and she knows he shouldn't have done it, but she is happy because she is hungry and now she knows she will be fed.

For many years now Railroad Bill has been stealing cans of food from the freight cars and sharing them with the poor black folks he knows. The railroad men and the police have tried to catch him for a long time. All the black folks know why the chasers can't come up with him. Once the sheriff of Escambia County and all his men started out after him. They ran very fast and they were getting close to Railroad Bill. As they raced through a little clearing in the woods they saw a black sheep standing there watching them run. They didn't realize until long afterwards that the little clearing was a strange place for a black sheep to be. Some of them don't believe to this day that the black sheep was Railroad Bill, but it was.

Another time the sheriff was out after Railroad Bill all his officers took a train to a lonesome place where they thought he was hiding. But Bill was in the car behind them all the time and when they got off the train and went looking for him he just stayed on and collected a lot of canned goods that he gave away all over Escambia County that night.

When that story got out all the people in the county laughed at the sheriff and that made him mighty mad. So he schemed as hard as he could to catch Railroad Bill. One day he was sure he had him. He followed Bill's tracks through the swamp and by and by he came to a little clearing, and no tracks left from there. So the sheriff decided Railroad Bill must be hiding under the low bushes in the clearing and he began looking around. Pretty soon he started a little red fox that lit out through the woods. The sheriff let go with both barrels of his shotgun, but he missed. After the second shot the little red fox turned about and laughed at him a high, wild, hearty laugh—and the sheriff recognized it. That little fox was Railroad Bill.

The time that made the sheriff the maddest, though, was when Railroad Bill chased himself to his best girl's house. The sheriff heard Bill had been courtin' a good-looking black girl over by Piney Grove. So he got some bloodhounds from Bob Gant over in Mississippi and he gave them a scent from one of Bill's old hats that he had dropped when he was running away, and sure enough the dogs started to follow a track right straight for Piney Grove.

By and by the sheriff said:

"Did we get three dogs from Bob Gant or four?"

Nobody seemed to be able to remember, but there were four dogs on the trail, and one of them was a black bloodhound.

When they got to the cabin of Bill's best girl the sheriff saw her on the porch and asked her if she'd seen Bill. She said, No, she hadn't for sure. The dogs seemed to want to go on, and so the sheriff and his men followed them. But now when the sheriff looked there were only three bloodhounds on the trail. The black one was gone. When the sheriff got home all tired out and took the dogs back to Mississippi, Bob Gant told him he had rented him just three dogs. The sheriff never *did* know that the black hound was really Railroad Bill who had chased himself all the way out to his girl's house and had stayed behind to do some courtin' when the sheriff left.

White folks say that the sheriff finally caught Railroad Bill. But the black folks in the woods cabins around Nymph and Volina and

Astoreth and Elwy and Keego and Piney Grove just laugh when they hear that and tune up their banjoes and sing a song that goes like this:

> Railroad Bill, mighty bad man,
> Shot all lights out of brakeman's han',
> Was lookin' for Railroad Bill.
>
> The old sheriff had a special train,
> When he got there was a shower of rain,
> Was lookin' for Railroad Bill.
>
> Ten policemen all dressed in blue,
> Comin' down the street two by two,
> Lookin' for Railroad Bill.
>
> Ever'body told them they better go back,
> Policemen comin' down the railroad track,
> A-lookin' for Railroad Bill.
>
> Railroad Bill mighty big spo't,
> Shot all buttons off the sheriff's coat,
> Was lookin' for Railroad Bill.

HOW JOHN HENRY BEAT THE STEAM DRILL DOWN

In the deep South everybody, white folks or black, has heard about big John Henry. Every state claims the contest with the steam drill happened inside its borders. People that live in the little towns of Mississippi—Hot Coffee, Hard Cash, Possum Neck—are sure it took place near Hushpuckena, but Georgia folks like to think it was over near Headlight, Georgia. This is the way a Georgia black boy told and sang the story to me.

JOHN HENRY was the biggest and blackest black man that ever lived. He spent most of his life helping white folks lay railroads, although once in a while he used to take time off from hard land work to be a roustabout on the Mississippi River. River folks who remember him say he could carry a cotton bale under each arm and two balanced on his head right up the gangplank, stepping off a fast shuffle to a banjo tune. And when the steamboat *City of Natchez* tried to beat the record of the *Robert E. Lee* from New Orleans to St. Louis, it was John Henry, they say, who sat on her safety valve to give her more steam pressure—and got sent a good ten miles in the air when she blew up. That didn't hurt John Henry, though. He landed on a wagonload of cotton bound for the gin over Savannah way, just in time to drop around and get a job building the Central of Georgia Railroad.

He hadn't been working for the white boss-man long before everybody in Georgia knew he was the steel-drivin'est black boy in the world. Every time he let his twelve-pound hammer fall the steel spike beneath it went down through solid rock another six inches.

John Henry could do the work of five strong men all day long and then go courtin' at night. He used to have to be careful not to use all his strength when he hit out with that extra-heavy hammer of his for fear he'd break the handle. Sometimes he used to use up a half dozen handles in a day. And his shaker, the black boy who held the steel spikes in place while John Henry hammered them down, used to bring along a pail of water to cool off the hammer heads when they got too hot from the fast whopping. When

John Henry was whopping the steel down just right, the water in that pail would be boiling from the heat of the head he had just been using.

One day a slick-looking stranger came to see Captain Tommy, the white boss-man, and tried to sell him a newfangled mechanical steam drill.

"Thanks," said Captain Tommy, "I've got a black boy workin' for me that can beat any machine ever made for whopping steel."

"I'll give you a steam drill free if you can prove that," said the stranger.

And so a great contest was arranged for a Monday afternoon. Folks came from all over Georgia to see John Henry try to beat the steam drill. Folks from Headlight and Ball Ground and Ida Vesper and Between and Black Jack took a day off to drive themselves and all their kin over to the Central of Georgia roadbed.

John Henry took it easy in the morning. His wife, Lucy, put on her best blue dress and brought him his lunch at noon. She carried their baby with her for she wanted the little black boy to see his father win and be proud. After he had eaten his corn pone and collard greens and pork chops, John Henry stood up and said:

"I'm John Henry and I'm a steel drivin' man."

Then the stranger got up steam in his machine, and John Henry spat on his hands and said:

"Bring me two twelve-pound hammers. I'm goin' to swing one in each hand."

His shaker brought him the hammers and John Henry was ready.

At the word "Go!" John Henry began to drive the steel spikes into the Georgia rocks. The steam drill did the same and for a while the two of them drove spike for spike.

"I ain't sweatin' enough," said John Henry.

The sun began to get hotter and sweat began to roll down John Henry's black back a drop at a time—then in little rivers. The two twelve-pound hammers took up a faster beat. Every time one hit, a steel spike bit another six inches into the rock. Faster and faster the hammers swung through the air. Faster and faster the steam drill puffed and struck. An hour went by, and John Henry began to draw ahead. Slowly at first and then swiftly he moved out in front of the hissing machine. He was throwing the twelve-pound hammers strongly as he bent from his hips with each blow. The cold steel rang like a silver bell each time a hammer struck. At the end of the second hour the whistle blew for the end of the contest. John Henry stood still a moment with both hammers raised high in the air. Then, like a tall black tree he fell to the ground.

"I've beat it to the bottom but I'm dead," said John Henry.

Lucy knelt over John Henry. His black head was in her lap. Sweat stained her new blue dress.

"Gimme a cool drink of water 'fo' I die," said John Henry. "Gimme a cool drink of water 'fo' I die."

Lucy gave John Henry a cool drink of water and then she placed the little baby in the palm of John Henry's big left hand. His right hand still clung to a twelve-pound hammer.

"Son," said John Henry, "you're goin' to be a steel drivin' man."

Then he gave the boy back to Lucy and he died with his hammer in his hand.

"John Henry, I'll be true to you," said Lucy.

APPLE COUNTRY

Sir! He who now accosts you has no contrivance to conjure up new associations of ideas nor to utter them in phrases novel or unheard before; yet if he did possess that power he would tell you how the recently imparted influence of republicanization would henceforward co-operate with the sea's phosphorescence to render it luminous, and with its salinity to continue it wholesome, he would portray freedom pervading the billows and rolling with every wave to the shores, and trace its workings upon the compacted continents and scattered islands comprehended within its embrace. Had he the ability he would observe that this renovating and regenerating would rise, by exhalation into the atmosphere, and impart some of its qualities; that it would impregnate the clouds and descend in rains and dews; that it would enter the vegetables and animals which constitute the food of the human race;—and that finally, the frame of man himself would be gradually so modified and mended by it, that at length even the sable and savage tribes dwelling in the tracts bordering on the Senegal, the Gambia, and the Congo shall lay aside their ferocity and enjoy, as we ourselves do, Liberty, under the guidance of the Law.

—S. L. MITCHILL, *at the Ceremony of the Mingling of the Waters of Lake Erie and the Atlantic.*

HOW JOHN DARLING WENT FISHING AND CAUGHT A BRIDE

The Upstaters in the state of New York are proud of John Darling and if you give them a chance like as not they will add a bit to the story of his surprising life. Although he was born down near the Susquehanna, in this story he gets as far west as Orleans County—a tolerable piece for a satisfied York State farmer to travel. You can hear about John in Adam's Basin or Penn Yan, Bouquet or Nightingale, Limerick or Clove Valley. Fish in the Oak Orchard River have really been known to jump into the fisherman's boat.

JOHN AUGUSTUS CAESAR DARLING —champion long-distance buckwheat pancake eater of the world, greatest sugarbush operator of the north, canal boatman superhuman and fisherman beyond all getout—is the favorite hero of many New York State stories.

Upstate folks tell so much about him it's a little hard to know where to begin, but aside from being born at Shandalee near Sand Pond and Livingston Manor, he got off to a slow start and never distinguished himself until he was about eleven. Then he was out plowing the lower forty one day when he drove his span of two pet steers right at a six-foot high stump. The plow split the stump, all right, and he got plumb through just in time, for the two halves sprang back together again so quick they tore his shirt right off his back. About a week later on a foggy morning John Darling's pa sent him up the ladder beside the house to shingle the roof. After John got through, the sun came out and showed him where he had laid the shingles on the fog twenty feet above the top of the chimney.

When he grew up John Darling had a long beard. Once a year, just before summer came, he would walk to town and get a shine, haircut, and shave. He always had the barber collect his whiskers into big gunny sacks and he took them home to his wife. She would throw them into the kettle and boil them and in that way she used to boil down seven or eight gallons of maple syrup that had got stuck on the beard during the buckwheat cake season.

As I've been telling you, John Augustus Caesar Darling was an A1 sugarbush man. He never used a sap pan that weighed less than a ton.

One morning he was out in the bush when he saw three mosquitoes as big as airplanes and singin' twice as loud making straight for him. He had just time to tip one of his ton sap pans over himself before they arrived. They started right in boring through the iron bottom of that sap pan with their bills and all three of them had got through and were prodding for him when John Darling got a good idea. He had his ax with him and he just split all three of those mosquito bills in two and then pressed each half back up against the iron surface over him. The result of that was that the last he saw of these mosquitoes they were heading off over the treetops toward Binghamton, and they were taking his sap pan with them. He never did get it back.

John Darling gave up working in the sugarbush after that and took to drivin' on the Erie Canal. The cook on his boat, the *Erie Queen*, was six-foot tall and redheaded. Her hands were as big as elephant's ears and her name was Sal. John fell in love with her at first sight. He made up a poem about her but she didn't seem to like it much—even though he recited it to her every moonlight evening. It went like this:

The cook she's a daisy,
And dead gone on me;
She has fiery red hair,
And she's sweet twenty-three;
She's cross-eyed and freckled,
She's a darling and a pet,
And we use her for a headlight
At night on the deck.

The trouble was that Sal had too many other suitors to give John Darling much of her time. But John wouldn't give Sal up. He just kept pestering her to marry him, and she kept saying, No. At last he thought up a scheme for winning her. He knew Sal loved to cook and eat fish more than any other food—and he pretty much fancied himself as a fisherman. So he begged her to announce that she'd marry the man who could catch the most fish in a single day—midnight to midnight. Sal said she'd do that very thing and she told all her beaux about it. Since there weren't enough fish in the canal for the contest, they all tied up their canal boats at Albion and went over to Oak Orchard River to try their luck. Folks came from all around—from Two Bridges and Eagle Harbor and Pretty Girl's Crossing and Checkered Tavern—to see the sport.

The whole lot of Sal's suitors started fishing promptly at midnight and by noon every one of them had as nice a mess of black bass and perch and pickerel and bullheads as ever a girl slipped into deep grease—that is, everyone except John Darling. It just seemed as though he couldn't get a single nibble. He fished and he fished and he rowed up and down the river, and by suppertime he had less fish in the boat than when he started, for he'd lost most of his bait. The sun set and the river got dark and the rest of the boys rowed down to Point Breeze to count their catch and see who'd won six-foot Sal—but still John Darling kept on fishing. All of a sudden he saw a bright light on the bank—it was Sal's red head. She had come out to help him—because she didn't want him to lose.

"Get in this boat," said John Darling, and when she sat up in the bow he could see by the light of that red hair a school of black bass swimming along just ahead of the boat. He rowed up into them and then suddenly turned into the bank.

"Put your head down to the water," he shouted to Sal, and when she did, the whole school of bass, forced against the bank on one side and scared out of its scales by the blinding light on the other, jumped high out of the water. John Darling swung the boat under them as they came down. After he had dug Sal out from under the pile he counted the fish that had jumped into his boat. There were two hundred and thirty-three.

If you don't believe it, just ask any Orleans County fisherman about the fish jumpin' in the boat out of the Oak Orchard River.

John Darling had caught the biggest mess of fish and won himself a bride. He and Sal were married the next morning and set out for their honeymoon at Niagara Falls. When they got back from their honeymoon they found the *Erie Queen* all decorated up with new red geranium window boxes and a big shindig going on inside to celebrate the wedding. The party lasted all night long and then everybody hitched up and there were twenty canal boats in line on the water and twenty span of mules along the towpath with all the drivers joining together in a song as they moved along toward Rome.

HOW JOHNNY APPLESEED BROUGHT APPLEBLOSSOMS TO THE WEST

Pennsylvania is proud that Johnny Appleseed chose to live in Pittsburgh, chose to take Pennsylvania apple seeds westward. You can hear the story in the old towns of Sky Beaver, King of Prussia, Bird in Hand, Seven Stars, Burnt Cabins any day you choose to stop off for a glass of cider and a good talk.

OF all the tales that Pennsylvanians tell, I think they like best the story of a strange fellow who rode into Pittsburgh on the lazy-board of a Conestoga wagon back in 1794. He said his name was Jonathan Chapman, and he built himself a log cabin on Grant's Hill.

It's a long time for a story to carry by word of mouth, but there are some people who say he told it around Pittsburgh that he had been born in Boston in the year of the Battle of Bunker Hill and that the first thing his baby eyes ever saw was a branch of appleblossoms outside the window of his home. If that is true, the sight must have influenced the whole rest of his life, for as soon as he had his house built in Pittsburgh he planted a big apple orchard. There, on the hill now known as Pittsburgh's Hump, the bees in Jonathan Chapman's hives made honey from the appleblossoms and Jonathan gave it away to his neighbors because, he said, the bees didn't charge him anything for it.

In the twelve years he lived in Pittsburgh an idea kept growing in Jonathan Chapman's brain until it got a powerful hold on him. He would take a load of appleseeds westward to the pioneers on the frontier so that they might have flowering, fruitful orchards like his own. Some folks say he would never have really got started with that load, that the idea would have stayed an idea, if Jonathan's girl hadn't jilted him. I met an old lady once who said of him, "He wasn't quite right in the head, you know; my grandmother called him 'love-cracked.' "

Whatever the truth about that may be, in 1806 Jonathan loaded two canoes with appleseeds and started down the Ohio River. When he got to the Muskingum he followed that to White Woman Creek, and he finally ended up along

Licking Creek where his load of seeds ran out. Behind him farmers were rejoicing in their seedlings—soon to be waving orchards—and they talked about the strange man who had brought them. They called him Johnny Appleseed.

Johnny went back to the Pennsylvania cider mills to get more seeds. They're still talking about him around Shadeland and Blooming Valley and Coolspring—the queer, blue-eyed man with long hair hanging to his shoulders, barefooted, wearing ragged clothes. When he had disposed of a second load and come back to Pennsylvania for seeds again, his appearance had changed still more. On his head as a cap he wore a tin kettle in which, when he needed it, he cooked his food. His only garment now, winter or summer, was a coffee sack with holes cut in it for his arms and legs.

Strange stories came out of the western wilderness.

Hostile Indians treated Johnny Appleseed kindly and helped him on his way.

A trapper had come upon Johnny Appleseed playing with three bear cubs while their mother looked on placidly.

Johnny Appleseed was entertaining frontier families by showing them how he could stick pins and needles through his flesh without hurting himself.

Johnny Appleseed knew direction by instinct and never carried a compass in the trackless woods.

Johnny Appleseed did not feel the cold of winter and could walk barefoot in below-zero weather without freezing his toes.

Johnny Appleseed had saved the people living in the fort at Mansfield, Ohio, from massacre by Indians, by running sixty miles through the dense woods in five hours to obtain aid.

Hundreds of Ohio acres were abloom with pink blossoms now, and Pennsylvania seeds had reached the banks of the Wabash. Everywhere Johnny Appleseed was welcomed by the grateful farmers. When he sat down at table with them, he would not eat until he was sure that there was plenty of food for the children. After he had eaten he would stretch himself out on the floor, take out the Bible he carried inside the coffee sack, and read aloud what he called "news fresh from heaven"—the Sermon on the Mount. His voice, one good housewife said, was "loud as the roar of wind and waves, then soft and soothing as the balmy airs that quivered the morning-glory leaves about his gray beard."

One day he trudged along for twenty miles to reach the home of a friend near Fort Wayne, Indiana. He sat down on the doorstep to eat his evening meal of bread and milk. He read aloud from the Bible for a while. Then he went to sleep, stretched out on the floor, and he did not wake up.

When the news reached Washington, old Sam Houston, Texas Sam Houston, made a speech about Johnny Appleseed in the American Congress. He said: "This old man was one of the most useful citizens of the world in his humble way. Farewell, dear old eccentric heart. Your labor has been a labor of love, and generations yet unborn will rise up and call you blessed."

This is just what the farmers who own apple orchards along Johnny Appleseed's path over a territory of a hundred thousand square miles have been doing ever since. And all the folks in western Pennsylvania bless Johnny Appleseed, too, for they know that when spring comes to the land known now as the Middle West hundreds of thousands of Ohio and Indiana acres will be pink and white with Pennsylvania appleblossoms.

HOW ANTHONY THE TRUMPETER DEAFENED THE DEVIL

Anthony the Trumpeter used to be a well-known figure in a little town called New Amsterdam. When that town finally became the big City of New York, the gleams of Anthony's trumpet and his nose faded a bit. Now they shine bright again through the years, particularly at Spuyten Duyvil, and in the region of a big town called Yonkers.

A GOOD many people who live in and around the City of New York are still remembering stories about Anthony the Trumpeter, although he lived many years ago. His real name was Anthony Van Corlaer, some folks say, but he was so closely associated with the big, shining brass instrument which he always carried with him that everybody called him Anthony the Trumpeter.

Anthony learned to play the trumpet when he was very young and lived in Holland. By the time he had come with his Dutch comrades to America and had settled on the Island of Manhattan, he was very good at it. He wanted to be a great trumpeter so much that he planned almost everything he did with that idea in mind. He ate and drank a great deal so that he would be fat and have a great deal of room inside him for the air he must blow out through the trumpet. And he never shaved for fear that he might cut his lip and not be able to play his beloved instrument. As a result of that he had a beard so long that it sometimes hid the trumpet, and folks were often surprised to hear a trumpet call sounding out of Anthony's beard without being able to see the horn at all.

One thing about Anthony was even bigger and shinier than the trumpet. That was his nose. His efforts at eating and drinking in order to make more room inside of him for air had for some reason or other made his nose larger for a nose than even Anthony's stomach was for a stomach. Moreover, the nose was of a deep rich copper color, and it shone in the sunlight with a great brightness. One time when Anthony was standing at the prow of a sailboat that was slowly making its way up the Hudson a ray of sunlight hit his nose and was reflected off toward the water so hotly that it killed a large sturgeon that happened to be swimming near the surface at the time. Anthony saw that the fish had been killed and so he dragged it into the boat and he and his friends cooked and ate all of it except the part where the sun's ray had struck it, which was too burned to make good eating. Folks along the Hudson were so much impressed by the story of how Anthony's nose killed the sturgeon that they named the big cliff near which it occurred Anthony's Nose, and it is known by that name even to this day.

Very few people realized how remarkable a trumpeter Anthony had come to be until one day hostile Indians attacked the Dutch folks on Manhattan Island. In the fight that followed, Anthony charged into the midst of the enemy and blew a long blast on his trumpet. It was so loud that all the Indians near by were at once struck deaf by it and they and all the rest were so frightened by the noise that they ran away and never came back. The Dutch folks felt a lot safer after that, for they knew there would be few enemies who would risk being made deaf by Anthony's trumpet.

Anthony himself came to have great faith in his trumpet, and it was this that finally led to his death. When Governor Peter Stuyvesant saw out in the harbor of New Amsterdam the boats of the

English fleet that had come to claim Manhattan Island for the British king, he sent Anthony northward to warn the Dutch folks along the Hudson of their danger. Pausing only long enough to say a fond farewell to each of the eight ladies who had claims on at least a portion of his affections, Anthony hurried to the upper end of Manhattan Island and arrived there about midnight. A storm arose as he looked across the Harlem River to the mainland, and Anthony realized that evil forces were at work to prevent his getting to the other side.

"I'll cross that stream in spite of the devil," shouted Anthony, and, with his trumpet slung over his shoulder, he plunged into the rough water which rose three feet on both banks when he hit it.

Anthony had managed to swim just to the middle of the river when an awful sea serpent suddenly attacked him. It was about three hundred feet long and twelve in diameter. It had a head like a lion's except for six eyes, three red, three green, as large as good-sized dinner plates and movable in such manner that he could see before, behind, and sideways. Four rows of teeth two feet long lined his mouth and a tusk eight feet long grew out of the end of his nose. Long ears hung down on either side of his head and he had a long curling beard. He sent jets of steam out of his nostrils fifty feet in the air as he moved. He smelled of sulphur, and the bushes and grasses along the banks near him were scorched with fire.

This horrible beast at once set upon poor Anthony and dragged him down under the water. Bravely Anthony grabbed for his trumpet and blew such a blast that even the Palisades on the distant Hudson trembled as though shaken by an earthquake. The serpent was so startled by the sound that he let go of Anthony for a moment and the trumpeter swam on—but not for long. The great monster seized him again, and this time there was no help for it. Anthony could blow no more and he was drawn down beneath the water forever.

But to this day there is a shiny quality about the water of the Harlem River at the point where Anthony the Trumpeter went down. Some folks say the strange light is from the trumpet, others say it's from Anthony's shiny nose. On wild and stormy nights, I am told, folks who live near the northern end of Manhattan Island hear a long trumpet blast, and they say:

"Anthony is blowing his trumpet again."

And the place on the other side which Anthony aimed for and never reached is called Spuyten Duyvil, which is the Dutch for "in spite of the devil," the very words Anthony used when he dove into the roaring stream.

THE BLUE SNOWMAN

On all the beauteous pendant globe no fairer, richer realm unfolds itself to tempt the angels down. No broader, grander, golden grainfields ever gladdened the heart and pocket of sunbrowned husbandman with hundredfold harvest and no greener pastures ever feasted the frolicsome mule colt or fatted the festive gentleman-calf. No mightier treasure houses of royal ore rear their proud heads heavenward in any land or zone. No bluer skies bend their sapphire arches above the far-famed beggar-hemmed and flea-gut bay of Naples or the Lake of Como.

No softer moonlight bathes in floods of silvery sheen the orange groves of Andalusia, or lures the gushing gosling to amatory squash-swapping with his adored-and-dorable-only ownest one. No balmier breezes sigh over Araby the blest or the Gardens of Girl in her bloom, than the sweetness-surfeited zephyrs that linger in loving dalliance amid our rose beds or pigsties, japonica-thicketed honeysuckle arbors and sewerage-soaked garbage piles. No bigger mosquitoes were ever broiled and served in restaurants down East as snipes on toast than those that industriously ply their profession along our romantic streams and lakesides.

No nobler, sharper, wide-awaker, straighter, tobacco-spitting, more enterprising, whole-souled, generous, truehearted and public-spirited men than ours ever left their stogie boot-prints on the golden sands of time. And no brighter, dearer, lovelier creatures ever flitted through Oriental poets' raptest dream of paradise than our blessed dimity divinities, our home-made calico seraphs, our patent inflatable-crinolined darlings, our Dakota sweethearts, wives, mothers-in-law, grandmothers, and cousin Mariannas who are creation's special pets and prides fitted to bear queenship in any realm. . . . Long live Dakota and the Dakotans!

—A Scream from the American Eagle in Dakota, 1882, 4th of July Oration by Col. P. Donan of the Fargo (D.T.) *Argus*, reprinted by the Chicago Milwaukee St. Paul Railway as a characteristic specimen of the fertility of the new Northwest.

HOW FEBOLD FEBOLDSON CURED NEBRASKA OF THE COYOTE PLAGUE WITH WHIMPERING WHINGDINGS

Febold Feboldson is a bit younger than most of the giants in this book but he is just as strong and smart. News of him and his adventures have been traveling about Nebraska from Lincoln and Gothenburg to David City and Red Cloud, Wahoo and Prairie Home, Northstar and Horsefoot. Perhaps he is one of Paul Bunyan's Swedish lumberjacks who has started out on his own in Nebraska.

OF all the folks that have made good use of the unusual animals in America, not one has done a better job than Febold Feboldson out on the great plains. Of course, some of those animals just can't be made use of—like the agropelter that lives in a hollow tree and keeps a lookout for people passing under its branches. When somebody does walk under the tree the agropelter breaks off the heaviest branch he can find and hits the poor fellow over the head with it.

The hide-behind is a useless creature, too, and very annoying. Whenever a man walks through the woods alone he is likely to be followed by a hide-behind. No matter how quickly the man turns around to look, he can never catch a glimpse of the hide-behind, for that animal is always a little quicker in jumping around behind him. The only way for anybody to get rid of a hide-behind is to get a filla-ma-loo bird to fly backwards just above his head and watch. The filla-ma-loo bird loves to fly backwards, and the hide-behind hates to be seen. The hide-behind will rush off into the woods every time he sees a filla-ma-loo bird flying backwards and realizes he can never follow it from behind.

Most of the animals I've mentioned are woods animals and wouldn't be much use on the great plains, anyway. Paul Bunyan once sent Febold Feboldson a wild hodag, thinking that Febold might make some sort of useful animal out of him. The hodag has a hooked tail that is very sharp, and Paul thought Febold could cut his wheat by just having the hodag run up and down through his wheatfield. Besides the help the hodag could give that way, Paul said the animal might help Febold get rid of the coyotes which howled so dismally every night that a good many Nebraska horses and cows got the blues and died of broken hearts. The hodag loves to eat dogs, and Paul thought it might eat coyotes, too. But the whole scheme failed because the hodag doesn't even like dogs unless dipped in a thin mud sauce and he couldn't find enough mud in Nebraska to season a single coyote. Then, too, the hodag has one short leg and one long one and can run fast only on a hillside. The flat country of the great plains confused him.

This failure to make use of a hodag didn't discourage Febold Feboldson, though. He thought and thought of possible ways to rid the plains of the mournful coyotes and finally decided that the best way was to give them a dose of their own medicine. So he got Paul to send him some whimpering whingdings. For a few days after the whingdings arrived conditions were awful. Whole herds of cattle heard the first few whimpers from these sorrowful animals and lay down and died of broken hearts. Thousands of horses listened and then drowned themselves in Dismal River. It was all humans could do to keep from crying their hearts out all night long.

But the coyotes were the worst. They were

so humiliated when they realized that the whimper of a whimpering whingding is just about three times as mournful as the howl of a coyote that they just lay down and died of shame and embarrassment.

The most useful of all the creatures that Febold Feboldson ever made use of, however, was probably the happy auger—a cousin of the dismal sauger who lives in the north woods. Men have been known to go crazy just listening to the "drip-drip-drip of the dank marsh water from the dismal sauger's cypress beard."

The happy auger is quite a different sort of beast from its cousin. It looks like a kangaroo for the most part, but it has a long tail shaped like a corkscrew. When it sits down it whirls around and around on its tail which goes down into the ground about six feet. When it gets up, then, it leaves a hole just the right size to set a fence post in.

Febold discovered one day that the happy auger was gun-shy and would jump fifteen feet in the air every time it heard a shot. So he had the bright idea of digging postholes with the auger simply by shooting off his revolver every time the animal sat down. If he took his time about it and kept the happy auger going in a straight line all

he had to do was to come along with some cedar posts, set them in the postholes, and string the fence wire.

Everything went very well for a while and Febold Feboldson became the champion fence builder of Nebraska. Then Old Man Johnson got jealous of him and tried to think up some way of beating his record. One day the old man was looking through the catalogue of a big mail-order store and came upon an advertisement of a machine gun. That gave him his big idea and he sent for that gun right away. When it came he took it out on the plains and waited around until he saw the happy auger sitting there, not being in use at the moment. Old Man Johnson began firing that machine gun a hundred and fifty shots a minute and that happy auger just lit out, jumping about twenty feet at each shot and leaving a perfect post-hole each time it jumped. In less time than it takes to tell it he was out of sight, and so far as I know he's still jumping. At any rate, Febold Feboldson can't find him and he mourns to think he can't make use of him any more.

HOW PAUL BUNYAN AND HIS BLUE-EYED OX STRAIGHTENED THE CROOKED ROAD

Maine, Michigan, Wisconsin, Oregon, all claim the best known of all American giants, Paul Bunyan. These few facts about him were obtained from Minnesota lumberjacks, who claim Paul prefers the woods north of Brainerd to any others. Folks who live in Good Thunder, Little Swan, Sleepy Eye, and Black Hammer can tell stories about Paul till the cows come home.

THE most famous citizen of Minnesota is one whom most outsiders never see—though many a good Minnesota lumberjack has worked for him. He is the greatest timber operator of all time, the best known of all American giants, a lumberjack so skillful that he could jump on a log floating downriver, spin it so fast that the bark came off, and then run ashore on the bubbles—and his name is Paul Bunyan.

Paul lives in the woods north of Brainerd and Bemidji, and he and his outfit occupy a shanty or bunkhouse so big that they have barbers stationed every quarter mile. At *that*, a jack bunkin' down towards the end can have a Sunday shave and not be able to get out the main door before he's grown a full beard.

Paul's foremen are all of Swedish blood because he says they make the best bosses. There's Olaf Olafson and Pete Peterson, and Lars Larsen, Jens Jensen, Eric Ericksen, and so on. Once Paul got fooled into making a foreman out of a jack who said he was a Swede named Murph Murphysen, but he turned out to be just plain redheaded Irish. With foremen like these and with the aid of his pet, big, blue-eyed ox named Babe, Paul Bunyan has made lumbering a fine art in Minnesota. Babe measures forty-two ax handles and a plug of Star chewin' tobacco between the eyes, and he is invaluable to Paul except when he makes lumbering difficult by drinkin' a river dry just when Paul is ready to let the log jam break and start a drive downstream.

One time Babe began to drink just as Paul let the logs go, and the logs all floated upstream toward the ox's mouth and puzzled everybody a good deal until they figgered it all out.

Last winter the folks at Bemidji gave a big three-day party to honor Paul Bunyan. Paul was off in the woods directing a big timber job, so the town had to be satisfied with a miniature concrete statue of him that was only eighteen feet high and weighed only a few tons. They had it wired for sound, and Paul broadcast his speech from the woods and it came out of the statue's mouth. They tried having Paul shout the speech without broadcasting it, but the sound came across three hundred miles much too loud and nearly deafened the Bemidji folks—so they had him whisper it into a microphone, and then, by toning it down some, they were able to hear it in comfort.

Folks came from all over Minnesota to that party. At Brainerd and Duluth the boys put on beard-growing contests in anticipation of the event. Some of them had to borrow their wives' curling irons to curl their beards up at the bottom to keep from stumbling.

Paul let some of his Swede lumberjacks come down to Bemidji for the party to take part in the chopping contests, but none of them could use a double-bladed ax and cut down two trees at once—one in front with the downstroke, and one behind with the upstroke—the way Paul does.

When Paul Bunyan organized his gang in the Minnesota north woods they were troubled a lot by mosquitoes. So Paul sent Sourdough Sam, the cook for the outfit, who makes everything except the coffee out of sourdough, way east for a couple of pairs of bumblebees that would kill his mosquitoes. Sam got his bumblebees in York State, strapped their wings down with surcingles, made them check their stingers with him, got them some leather shoes, and brought them to Minnesota overland on foot without the loss of a single bee. When they got there, though, Paul found out he'd miscalculated, for instead of killing the mosquitoes, the bumblebees fell in love with them and married them. Their children all grew up with stingers both before and behind, and life was worse than ever until they smelled a boatload of sugar out in the middle of Lake Superior on its way to Duluth. Having inherited a taste for sweets from their bumblebee forefathers, they all set out for it and loaded themselves so heavy that when they tried to fly ashore they couldn't make it, and were all drowned.

Paul has never been much of a hand with the ladies—that is, until recently. The first time he was ever attracted to a female, he fell in love with a pretty girl from Utah. When he found out that she was married—as most pretty Utah girls were at the time—he sat down and cried, he was that disappointed.

Great Salt Lake is nothing but a big hollow filled up with Paul Bunyan's tears.

Paul's first wife was a caution. She was as ugly as sin and she had a wooden leg—but she was a powerful woman. Paul ran onto her one day when he heard a scream and saw her trying to rescue her sister who had fallen into the Mississippi and was being carried down the rapids to a high falls. Paul grabbed a shovel and threw enough dirt into the river to make a dam just behind the girl. His future wife helped, and in no time at all the girl began to drag on bottom and then she stood up and walked to the bank. Paul thought a strong digger like the girl who helped pile up the dam would be a great aid to him, and he married her. She turned out to be a good cook, specializing in double-holed doughnuts. Once she dropped her false teeth into Rainy Lake, and Paul got them back for her by using a fishline with one of those doughnuts tied on the end for bait. He lowered the doughnut right over those teeth, and all of a sudden they snapped into it, and Paul pulled them up to the surface.

That first wife of Paul's was a mean woman,

and she finally ran away with an Irish lumberjack who made goo-goo eyes at her. Paul got a divorce, and now folks say he's got a wife that he carved out of the inside of a birch log. He cut her out just to suit himself, and those that have seen her say she has a beautiful figure and a pretty face, though her nose is a little short and uptilted because just at that point Paul's knife slipped. Paul doesn't let her come around camp, though, because he remembers what happened to his first wife and he knows how a lumberjack just can't help making himself attractive to a woman whenever he sees her.

There are hundreds of other tales of Paul Bunyan and his blue-eyed ox Babe that I'd like to tell you. There was the time Paul hitched Babe to a logging road so crooked that people used to meet themselves suddenly on turning a curve in it. Babe pulled and yanked so hard that the road finally gave way and came out straight as a crow's flight. It was only eight miles long after it was straightened, and Paul had fifty-eight miles left over that he smoothed out, shined up, and made into one of the prettiest boulevards you ever saw. He gave it to the city of Minneapolis. Folks there call it Grand Rounds, but it really ought to be

Paul Bunyan Boulevard in honor of the man who made it and handed it over.

That boulevard reminds me of one of Paul's best known adventures because it comes back just where it started from. One time Paul put Jim Liverpool in charge of a drive and saw him and his gang off, driving a big jam downriver. They were gone two months and then showed up, still driving strong, right beside Paul's camp.

"We were by here once before last month," said Jim. "At least, we went by a camp that looked just like this."

Paul scratched his head. Then he said:

"I've got it. You've been driving those logs on Round River. It flows in a complete circle, and you've been around it twice."

He called to Sourdough Sam and told him to mix up a mess of batter and pour it into the river. Sam had it ready in no time and as soon as it hit the water the batter began to rise and swell. In an hour's time it had made as pretty a dam as you ever saw and the waters in Round River had risen high over their banks and were carrying those logs straight as a string into the Crow Wing River.

BIBLIOGRAPHY

ASBURY, HERBERT, *The French Quarter*. New York: Alfred A. Knopf, Inc., 1936.

BEATH, PAUL R., *Legends of Febold Feboldson*. Federal Writers' Project in Nebraska, 1937.

BLAIR, WALTER, and MEINE, FRANKLIN J., *Mike Fink: King of Mississippi Keelboatmen*. New York: Henry Holt and Company, 1933.

BOTKIN, B. A. (editor), *Folk-say, a Regional Miscellany*. Norman: Oklahoma Folk-Lore Society, 1929-1932.

BOWMAN, JAMES CLOYD, *Pecos Bill: the Greatest Cowboy of All Time*. Chicago, Illinois: Albert Whitman & Company, 1937.

BROWN, CHARLES EDWARD, *Paul Bunyan and Tony Beaver Tales*. Madison, Wisconsin: C. E. Brown.

BURGESS, W. F., *Dr. Valentine and Yankee Hill's Metamorphoses*. New York: W. F. Burgess, 1850.

DAUGHERTY, JAMES H., *Their Weight in Wildcats*. Boston: Houghton Mifflin Company, 1936.

DIGGES, JEREMIAH, *The Cape Cod Pilot*. Modern Pilgrim Press, Provincetown, Massachusetts (Federal Writers' Project), 1937.

DOBIE, J. FRANK (editor), *The Publications of the Texas Folk-Lore Society*. Austin, Texas.

Hudson, Arthur Palmer (editor), *Humor of the Old Deep South.* New York: The Macmillan Company, 1936.

Lockwood, Frank C., *Pioneer Days in Arizona.* New York: The Macmillan Company, 1932.

McDanield, H. F., and Taylor, N. A., *The Coming Empire; or, Two Thousand Miles in Texas on Horseback.* Dallas, Texas: Col. Nathanial Alston Taylor, 1936. New York: A. S. Barnes and Company, 1877.

McHugh, Vincent, *Caleb Catlum's America.* New York: Stackpole Sons, 1936.

Montague, Margaret Prescott, *Up Eel River.* New York: The Macmillan Company, 1928.

Red River Lumber Company, *Tales About Paul Bunyan.* Chicago, Illinois.

Rourke, Constance, *Davy Crockett.* New York: Harcourt, Brace and Company, 1934.

Roy, L. M. A., *Ocean-Born Mary.* Privately printed at the Ocean-Born Mary House, Henniker, New Hampshire, 1935.

Sandburg, Carl, *Abraham Lincoln.* New York: Harcourt, Brace and Company, 1926.

Shay, Frank, *Here's Audacity! American Legendary Heroes.* New York: The Macaulay Company, 1930.

Shepard, Esther, *Paul Bunyan.* Seattle, Washington: The McNeil Press, 1924.

Skinner, C. M., *Myths and Legends of Our Own*

Land. Philadelphia, Pennsylvania: J. B. Lippincott Company, 1896.

STEVENS, JAMES, *Paul Bunyan*. New York: Alfred A. Knopf, Inc., 1925.

WRIGHT, RICHARDSON, *Hawkers and Walkers in Early America*. Philadelphia, Pennsylvania: J. B. Lippincott Company, 1927.